GORILLA PICTURES AND PHOTOGRAPHY - A GORILLAS PICTURE AND PHOTO BOOK - AMAZING BIG COLLECTION

GORILLAS

EDITED BY

JANA VILLANEUVA

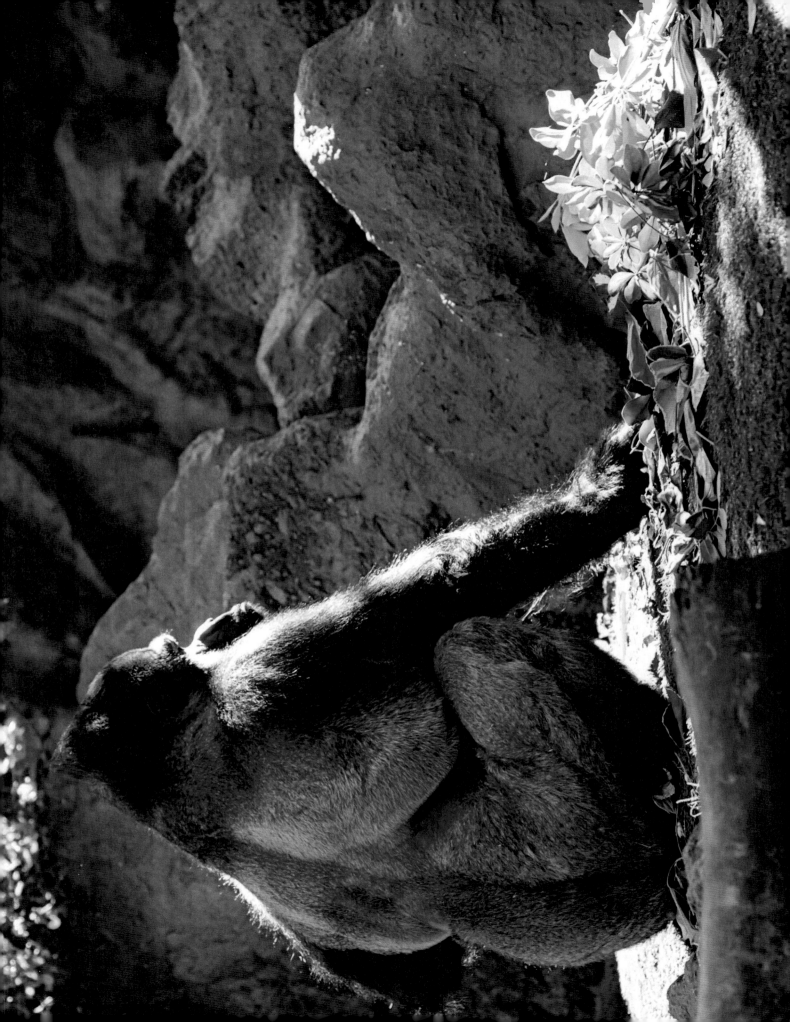

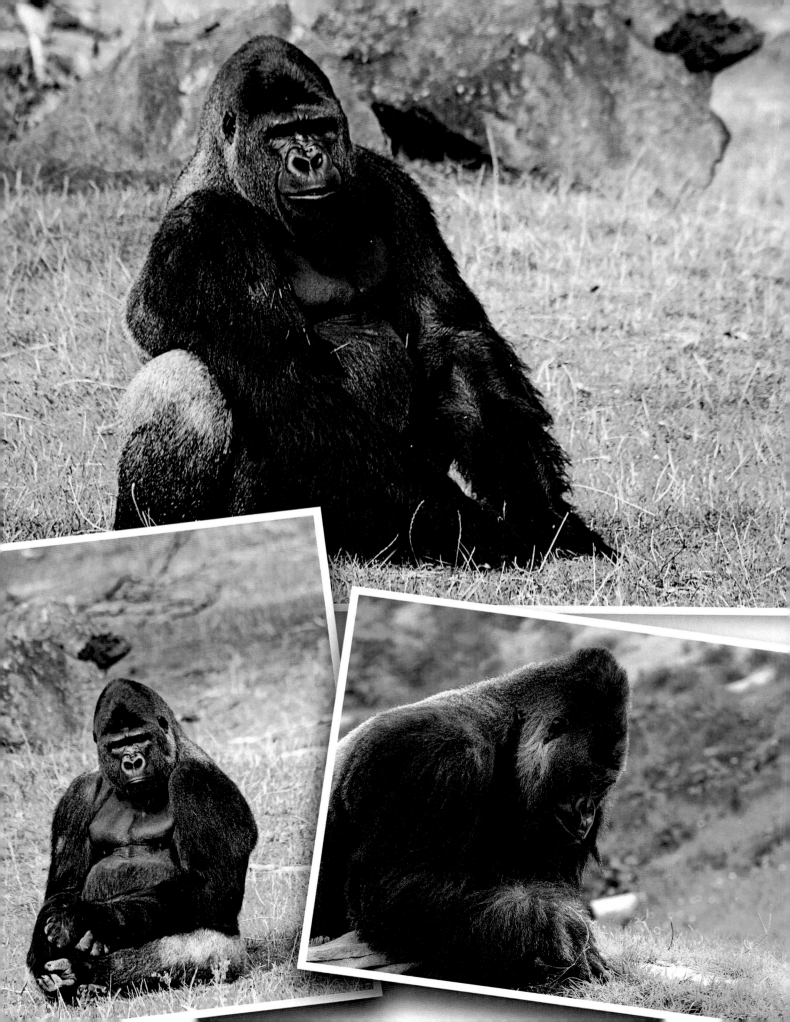

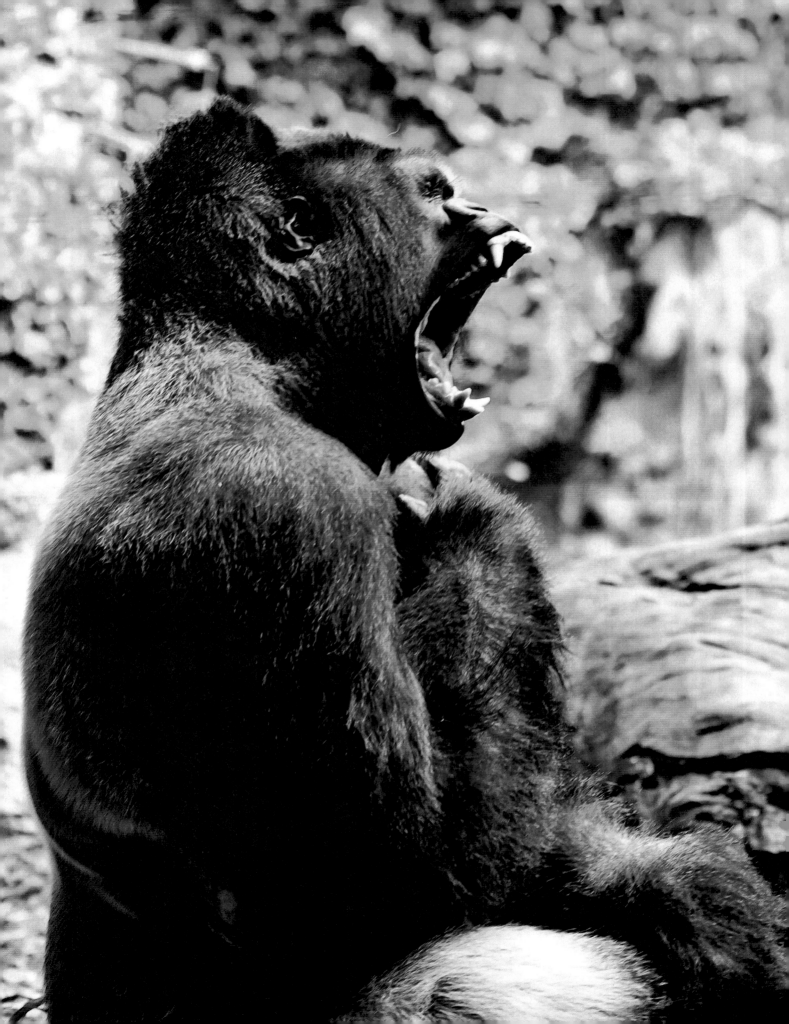

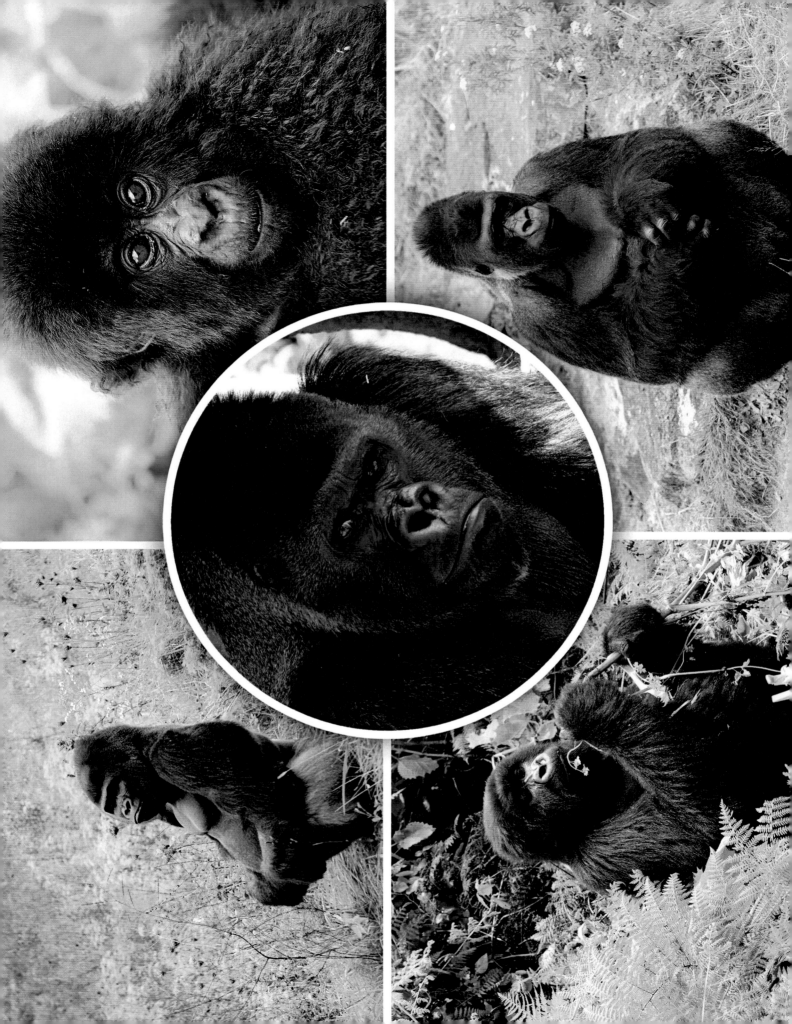

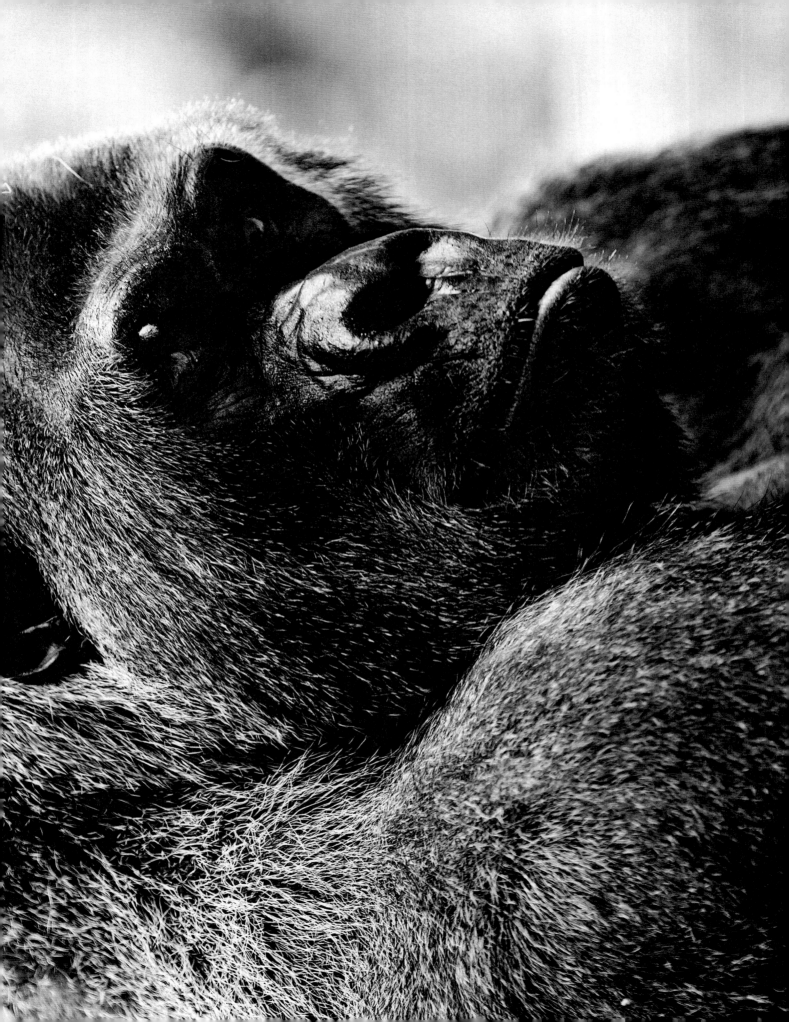

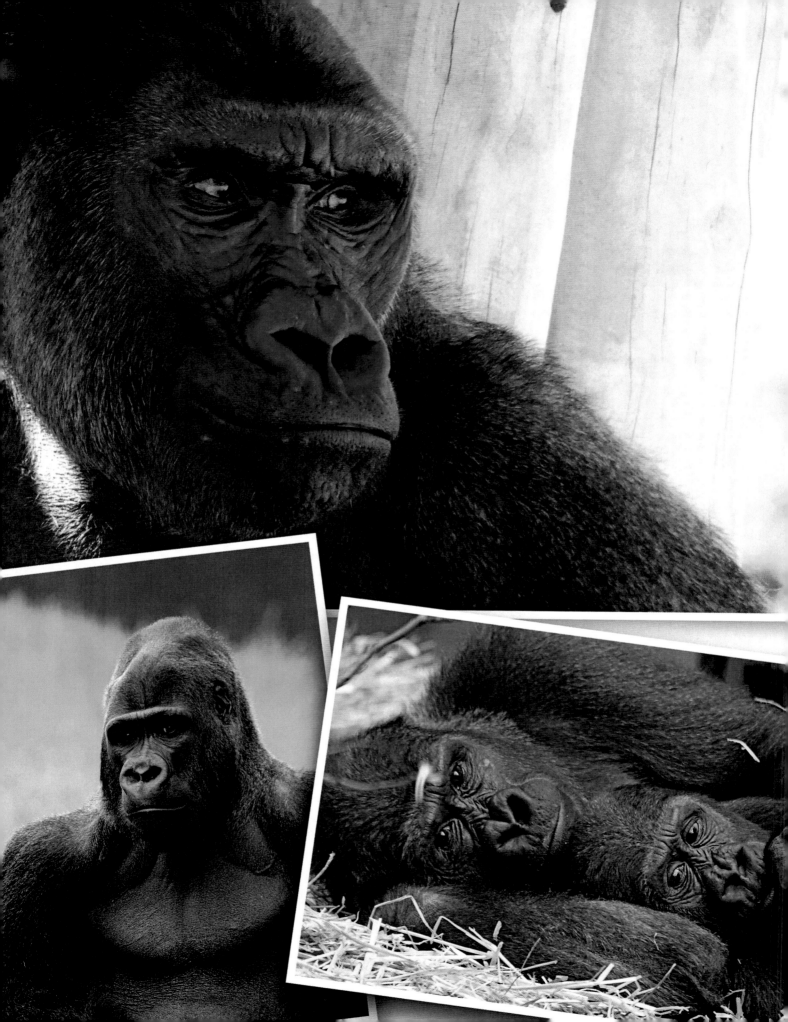

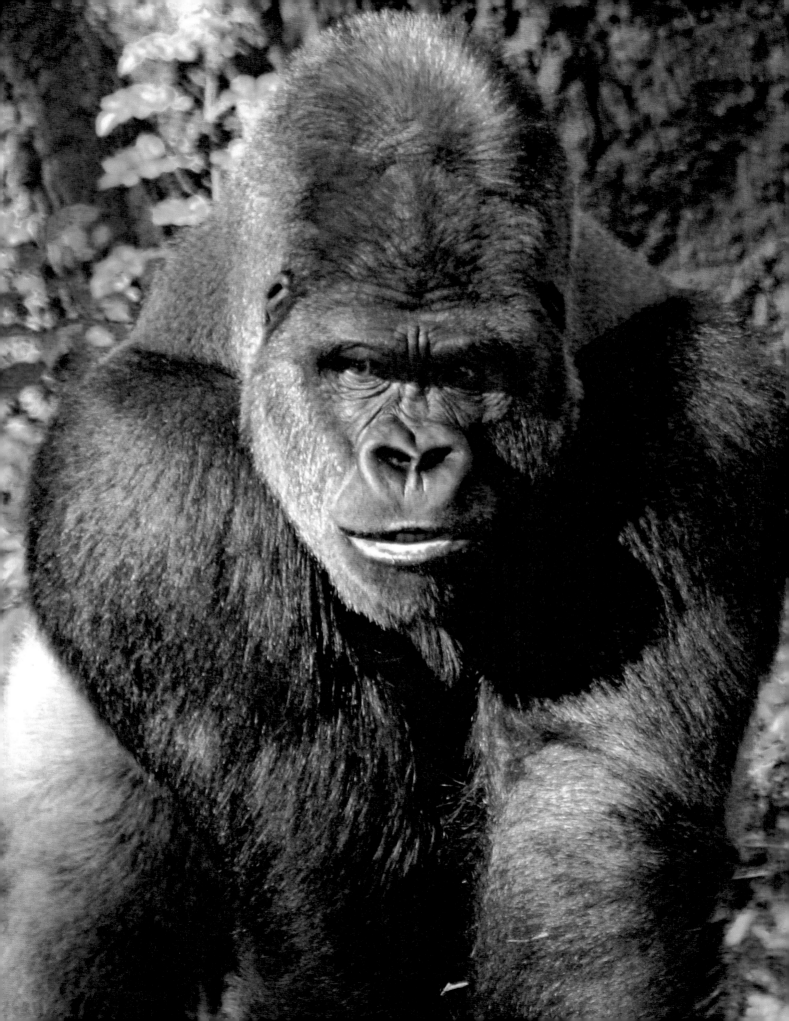

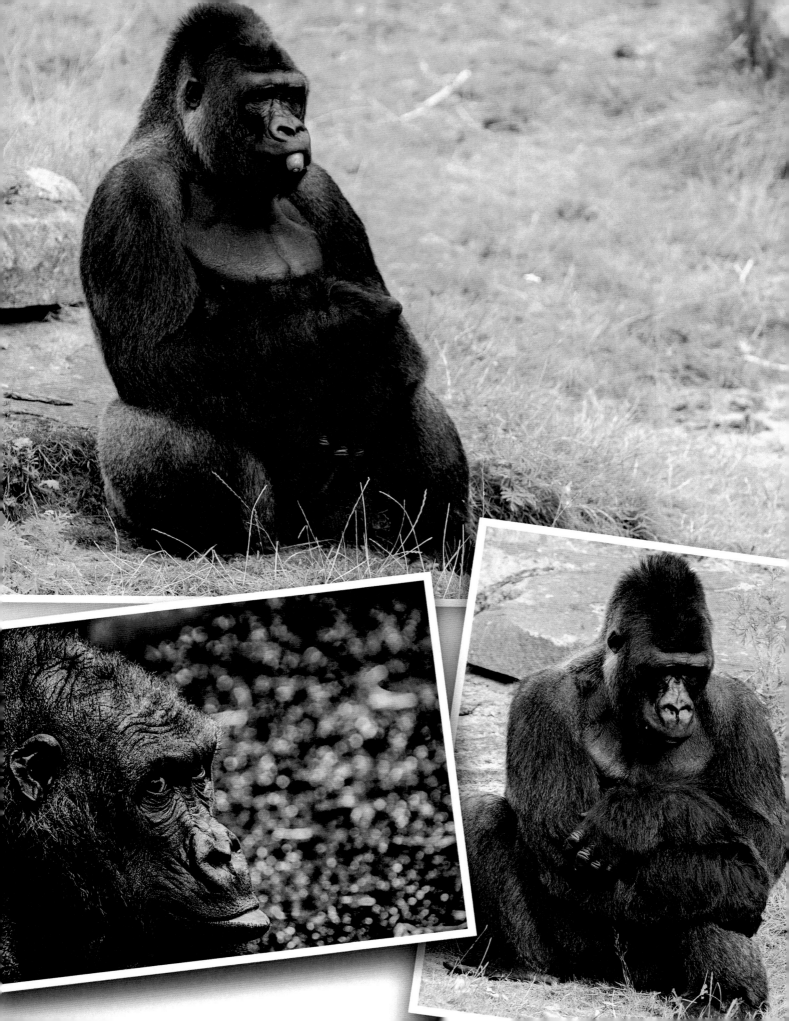

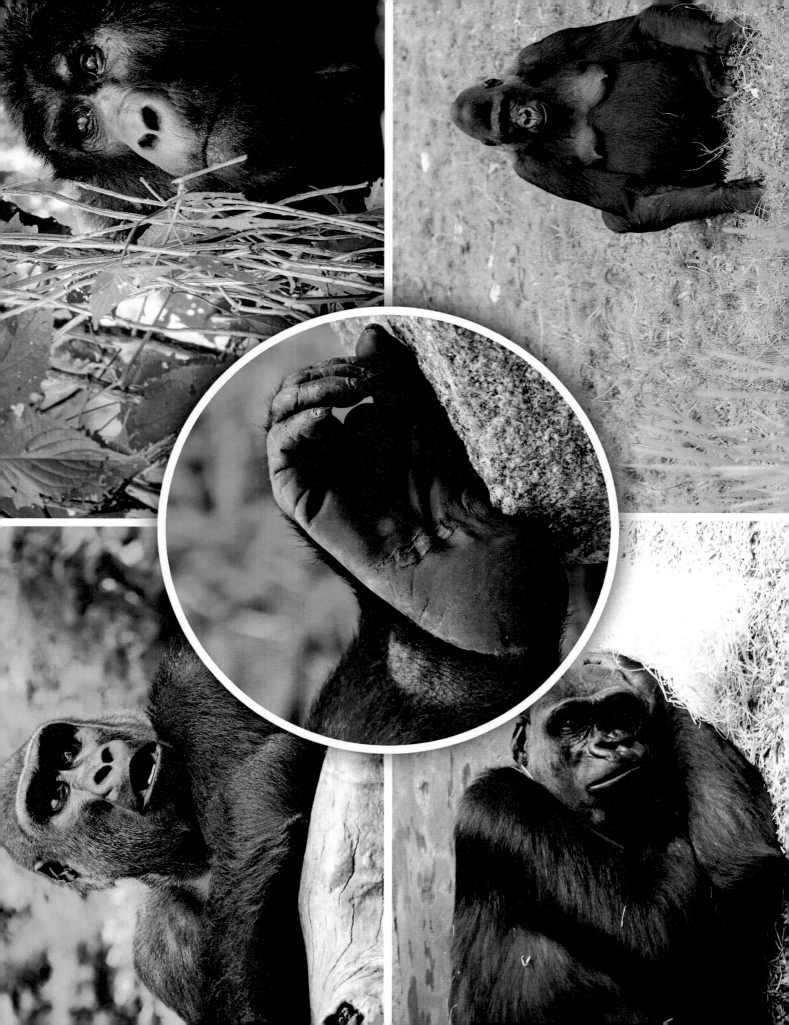

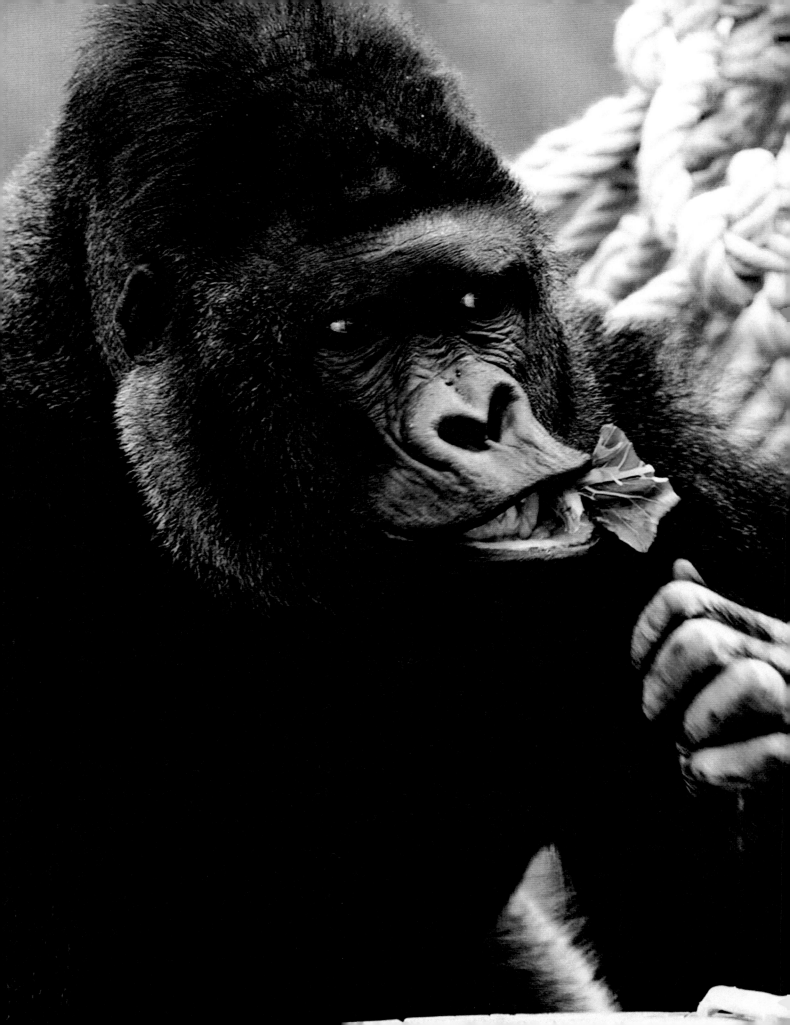

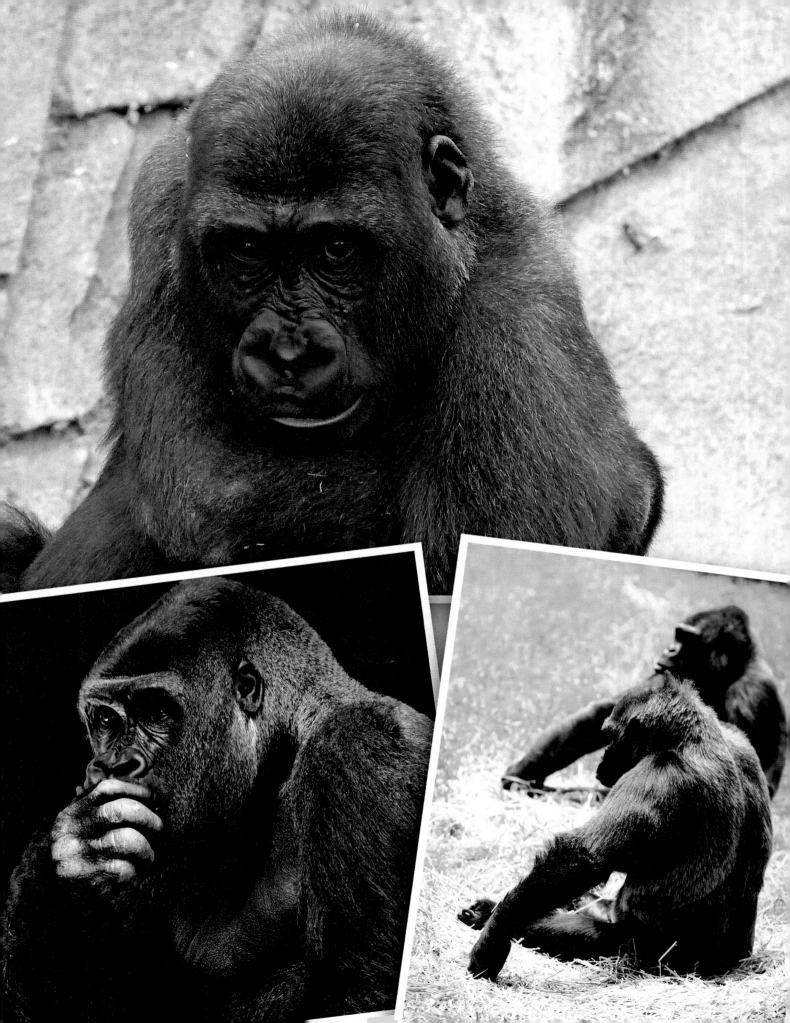

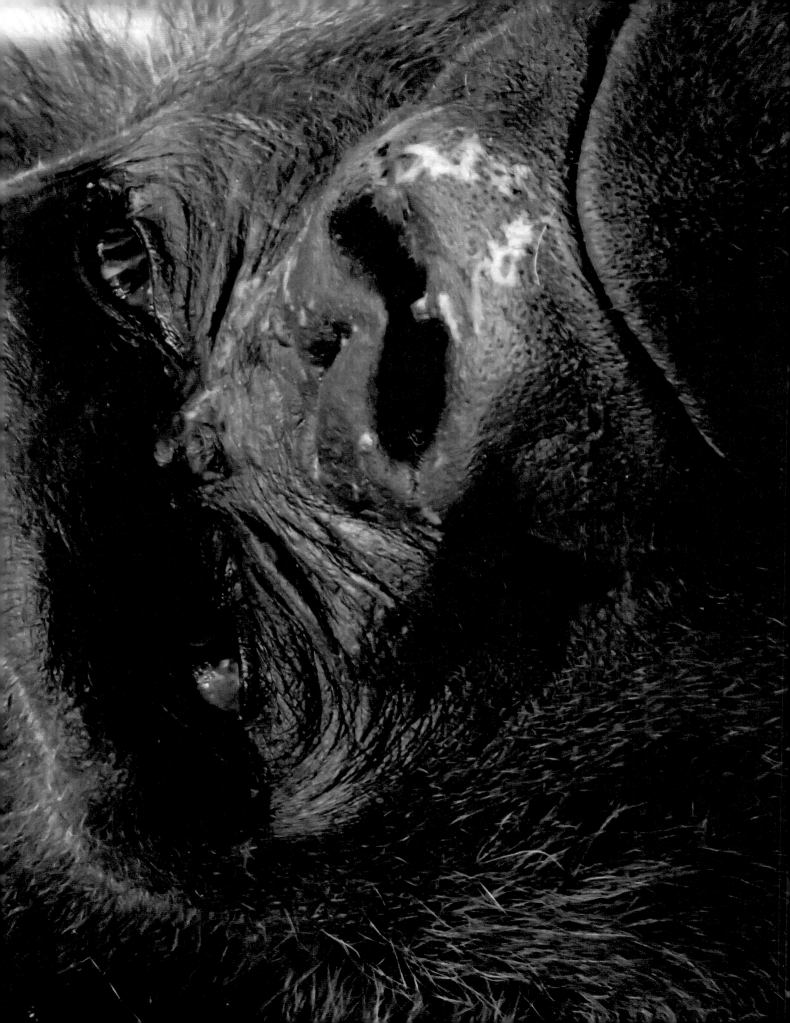

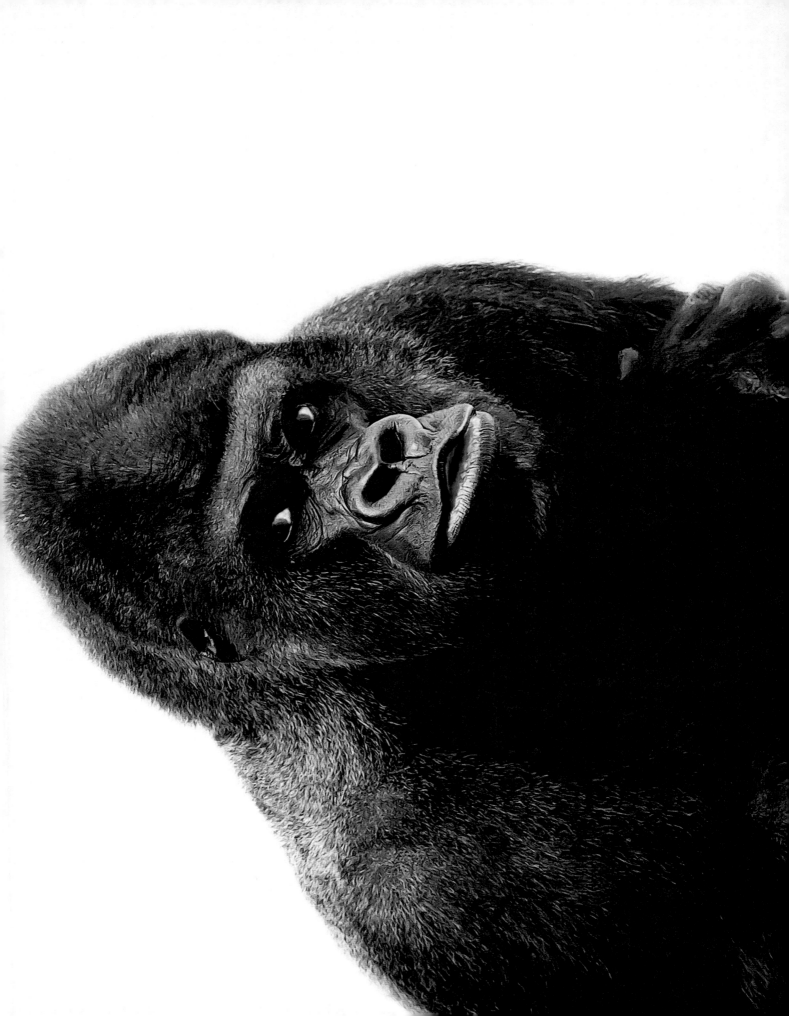

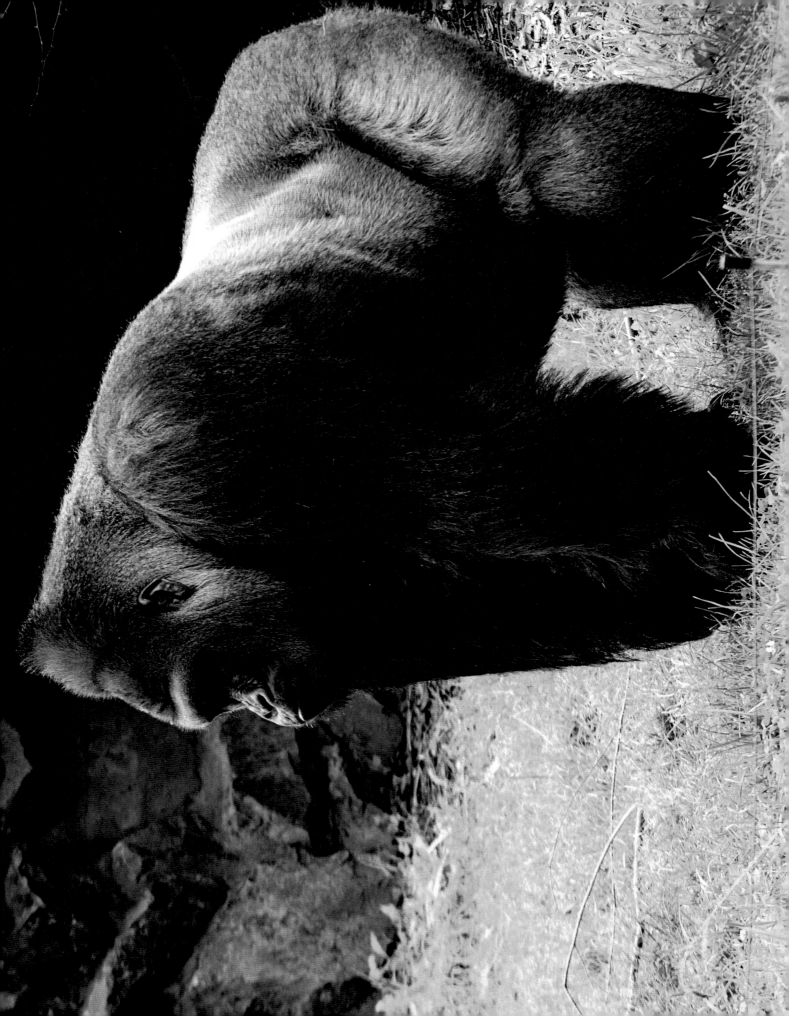

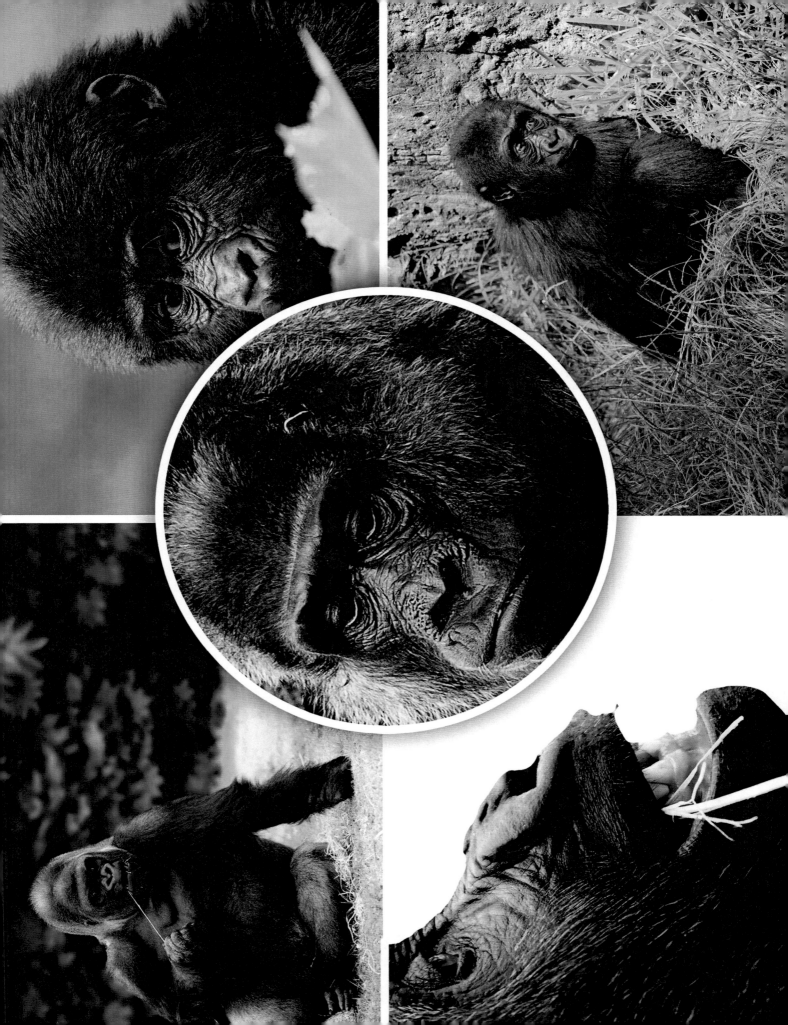

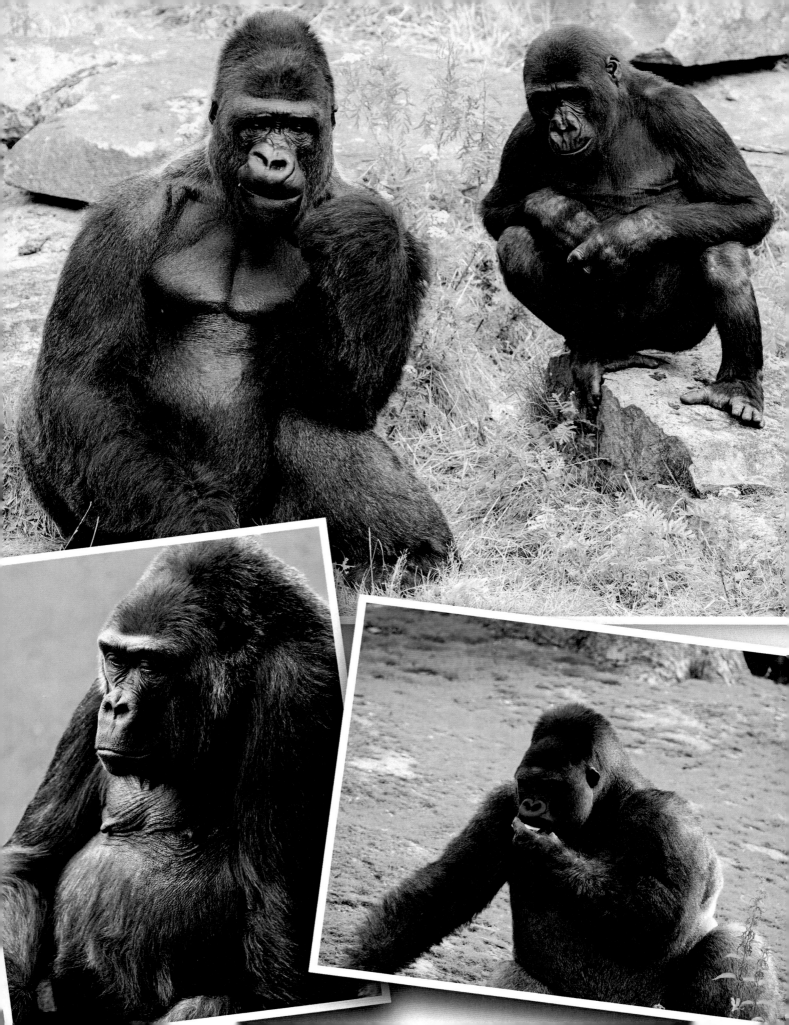

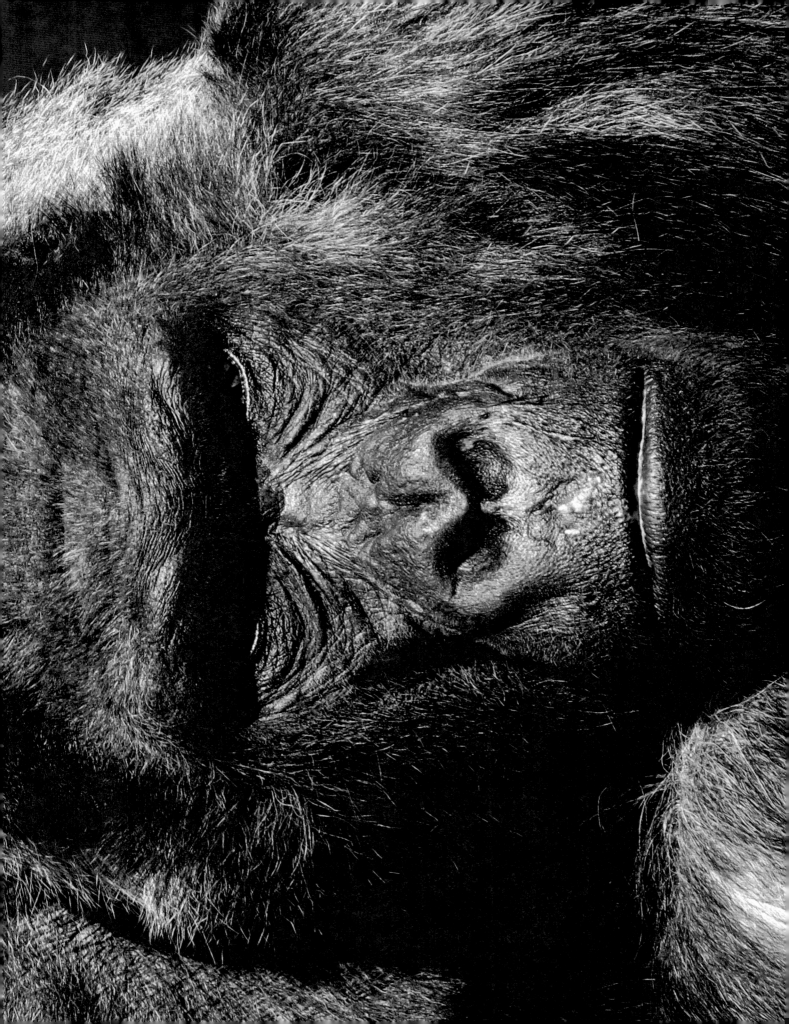

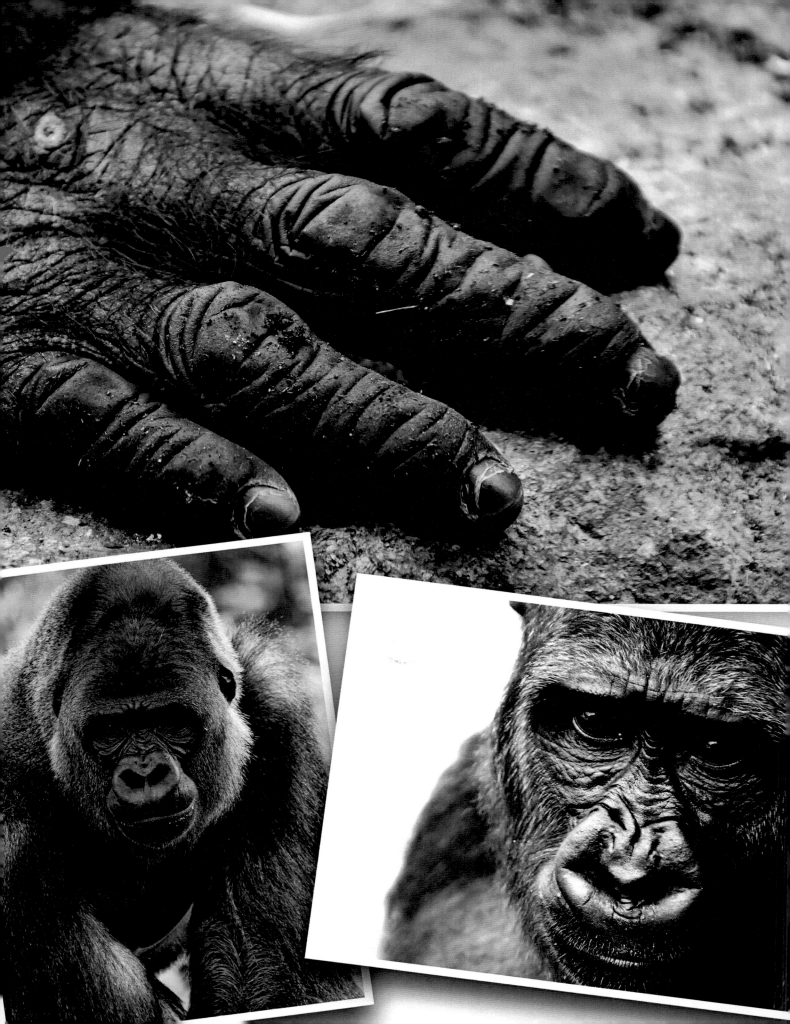

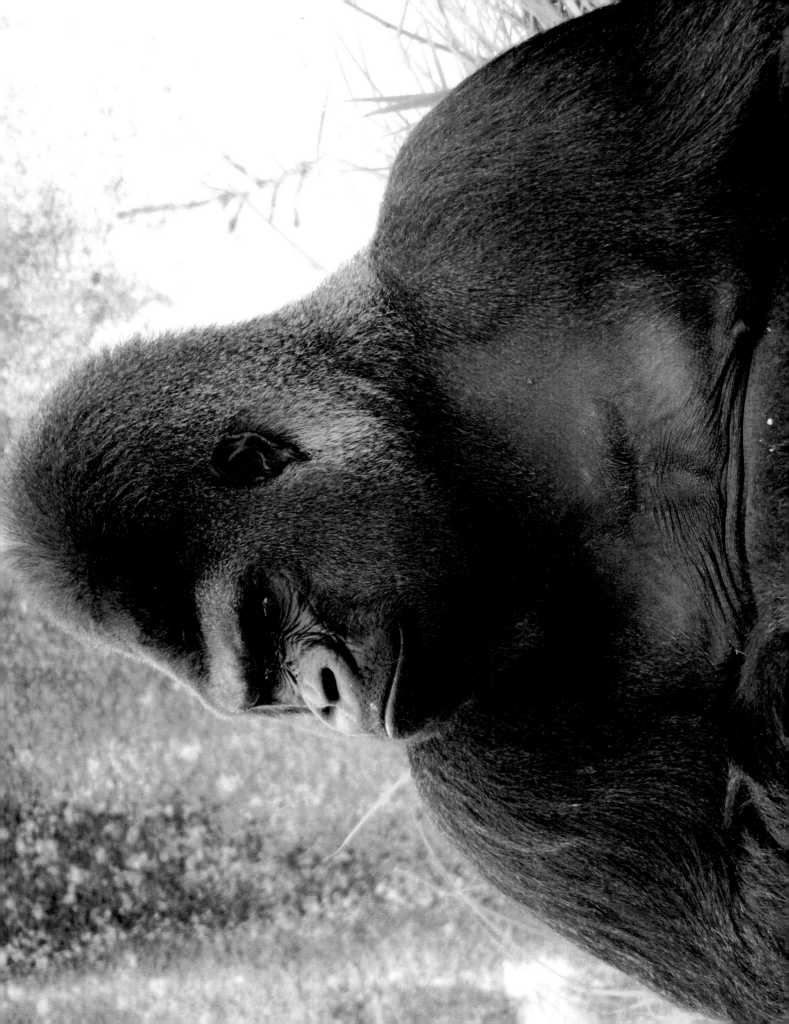

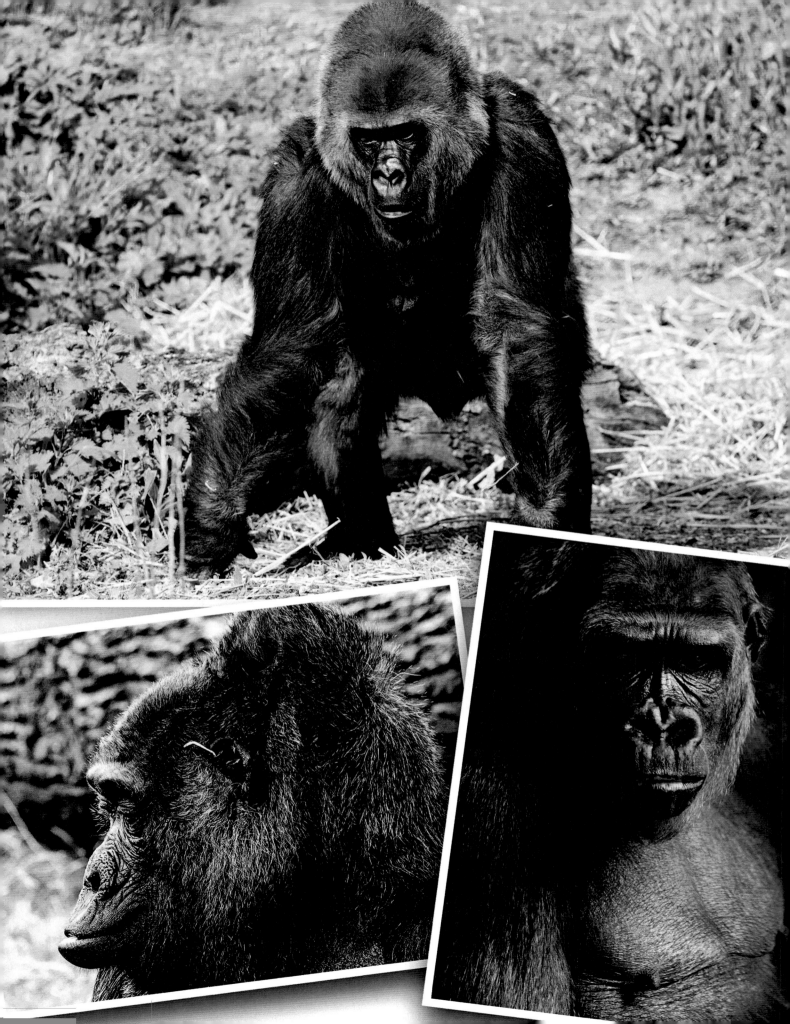

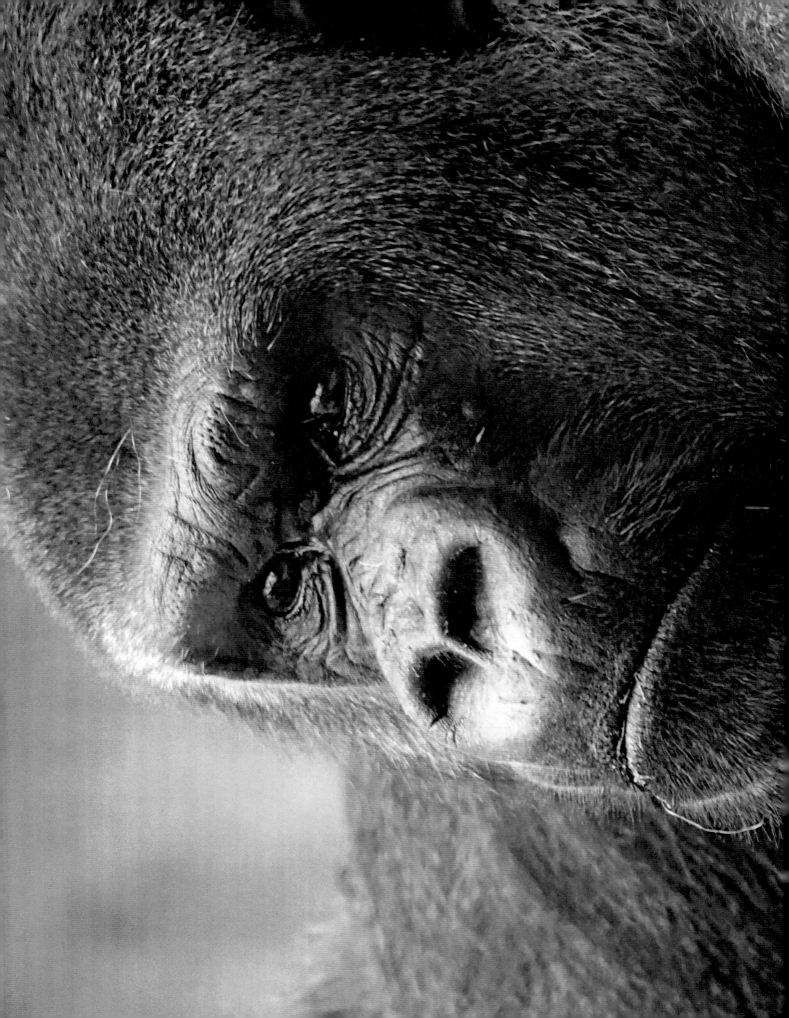

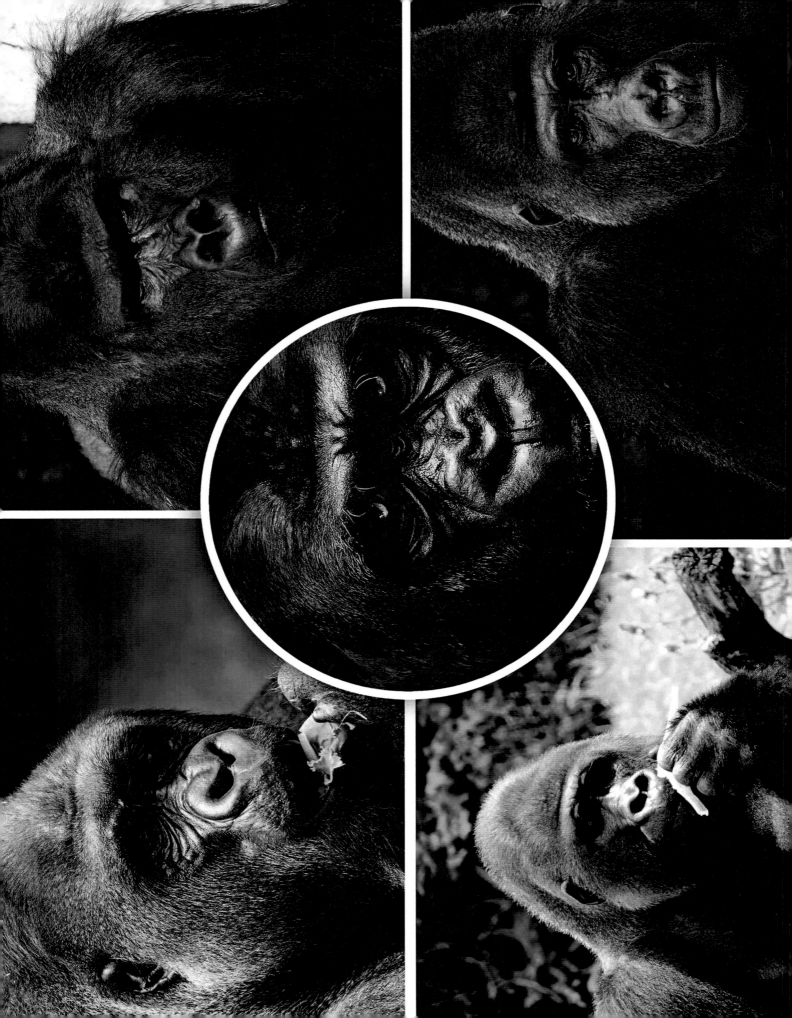

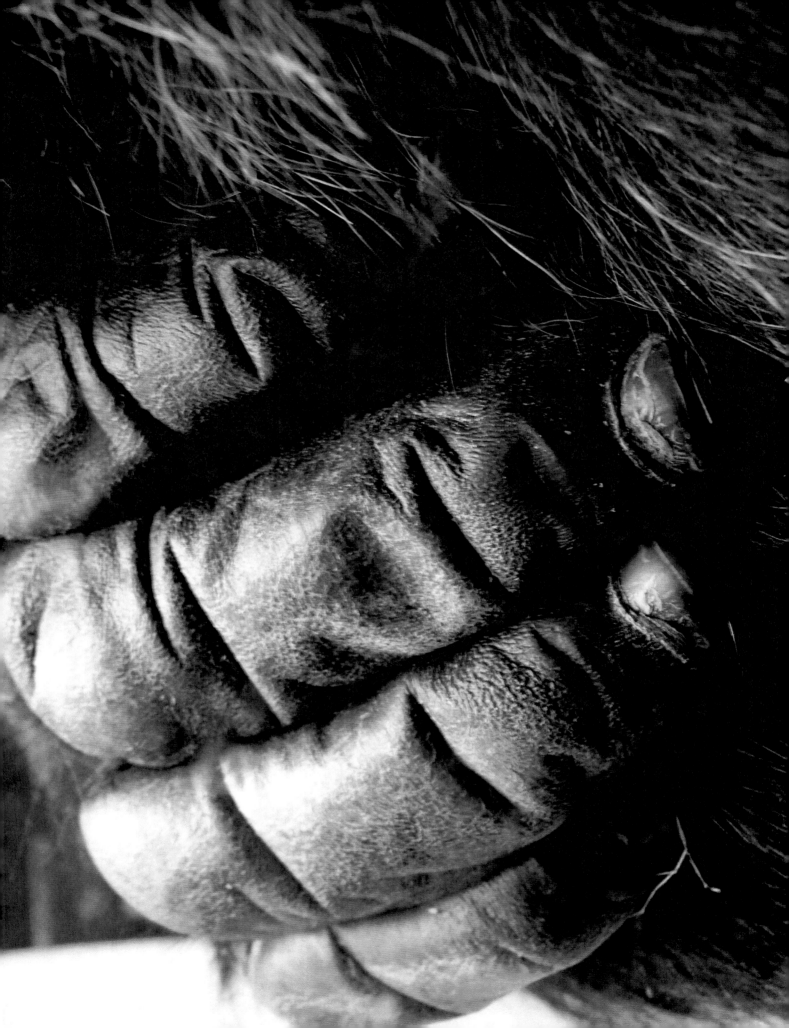

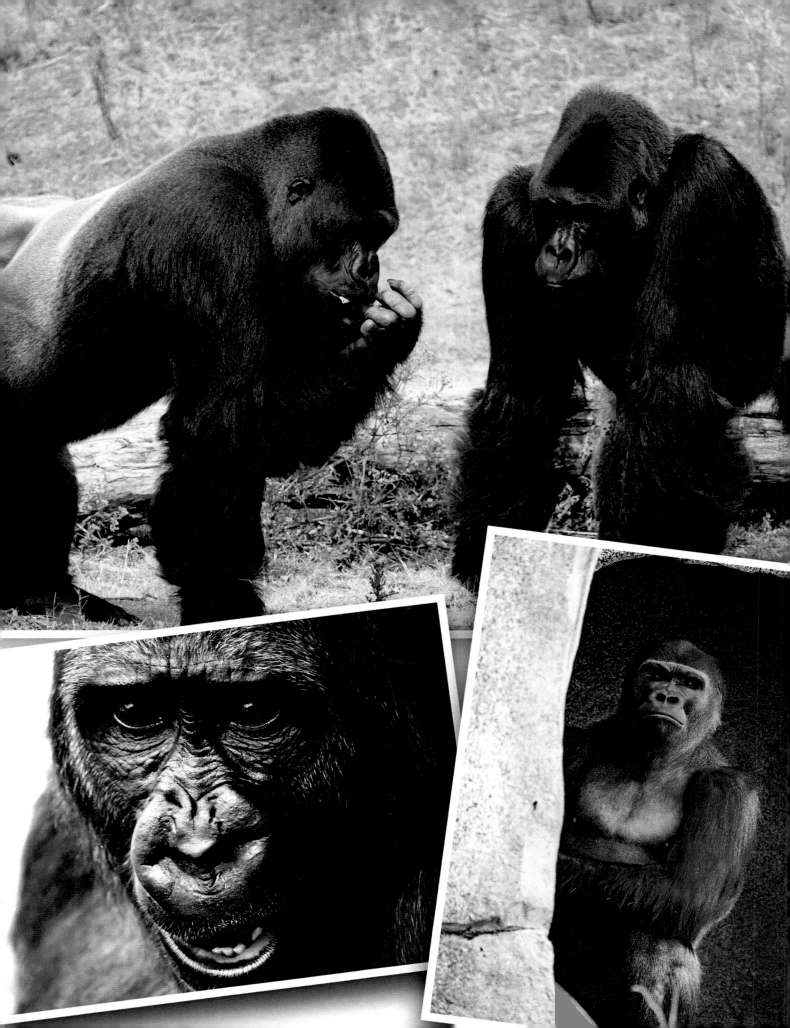

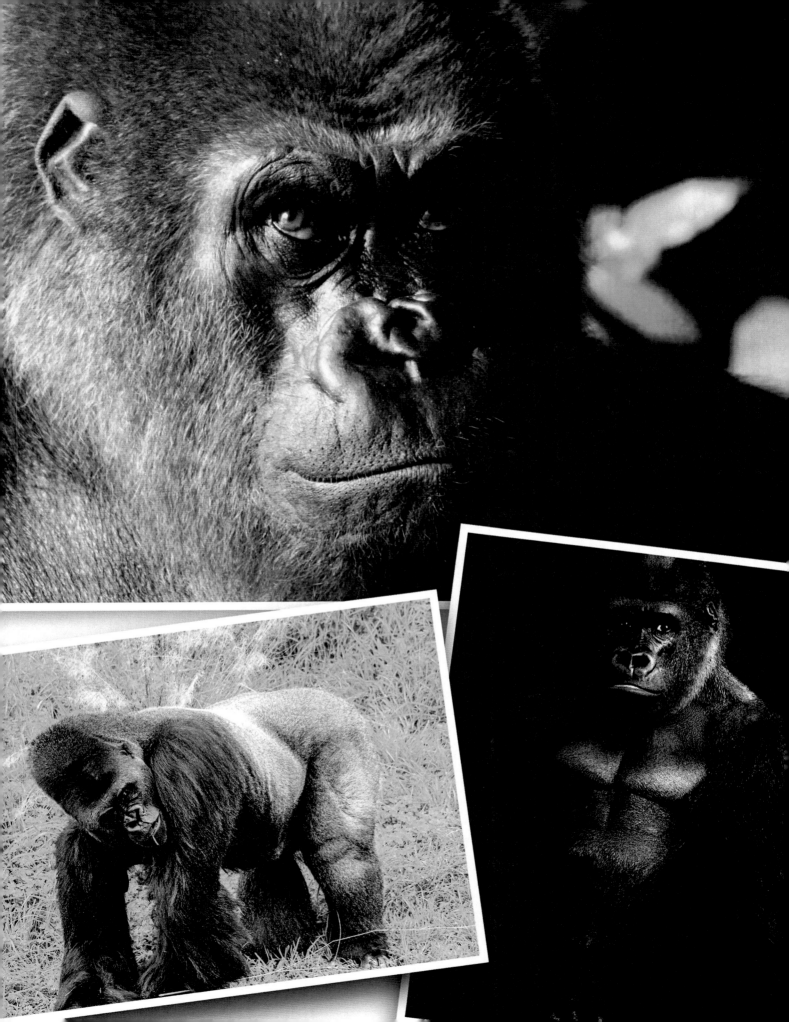

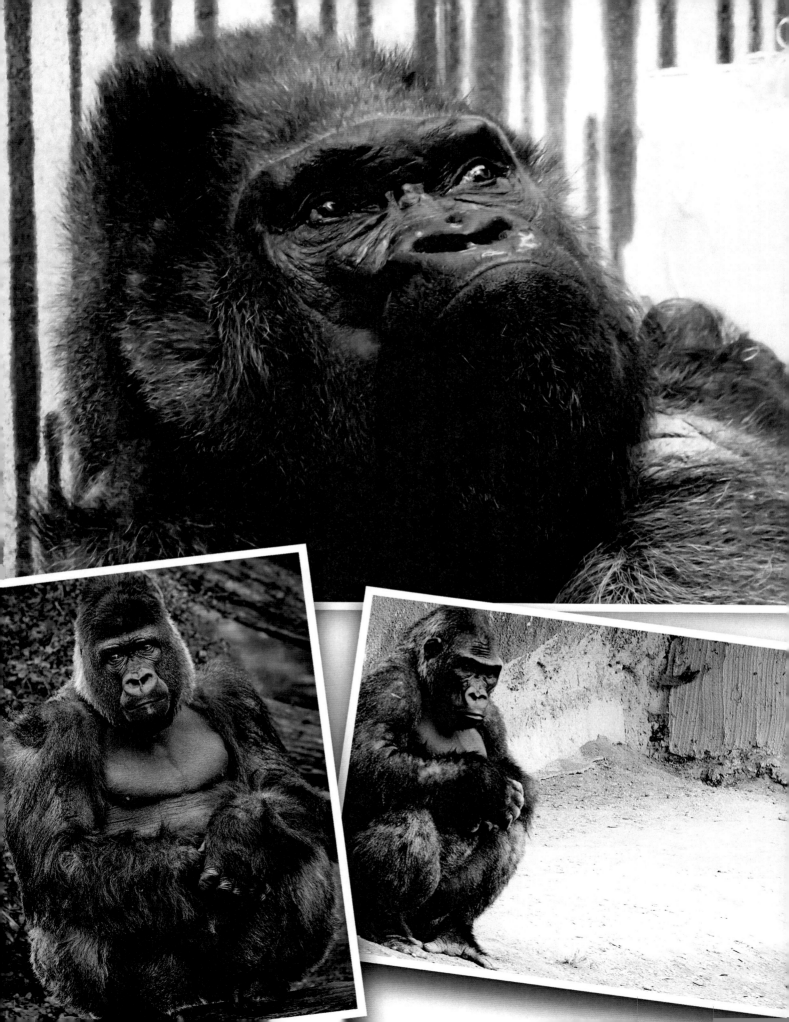

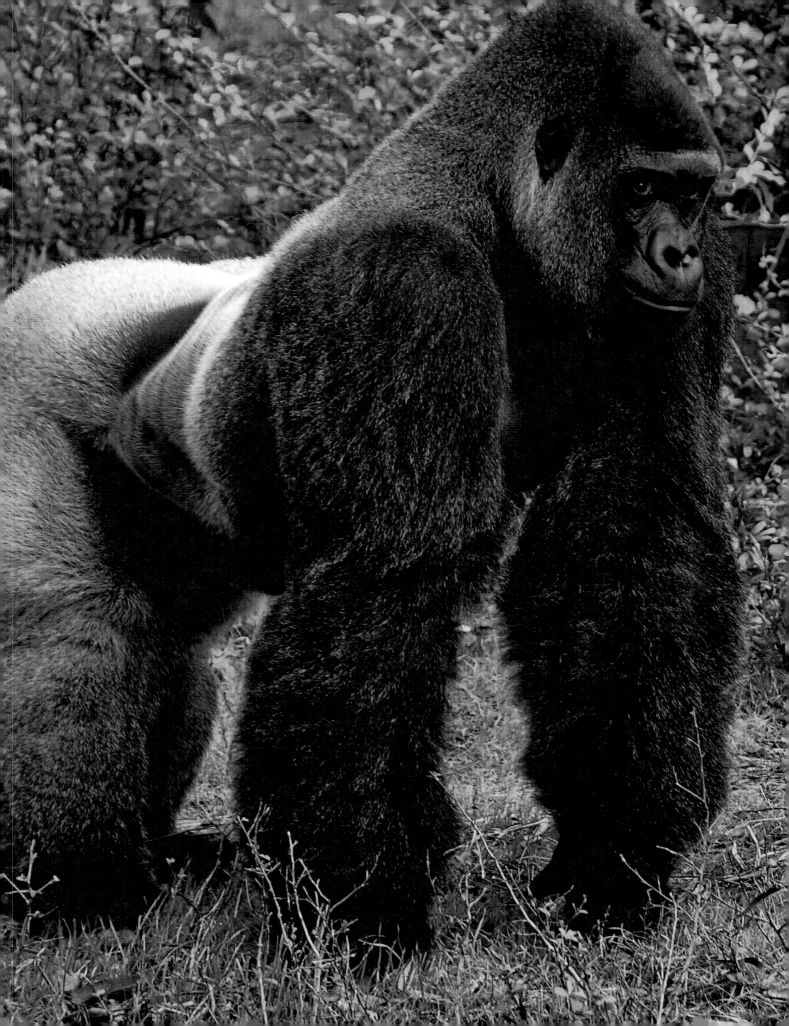

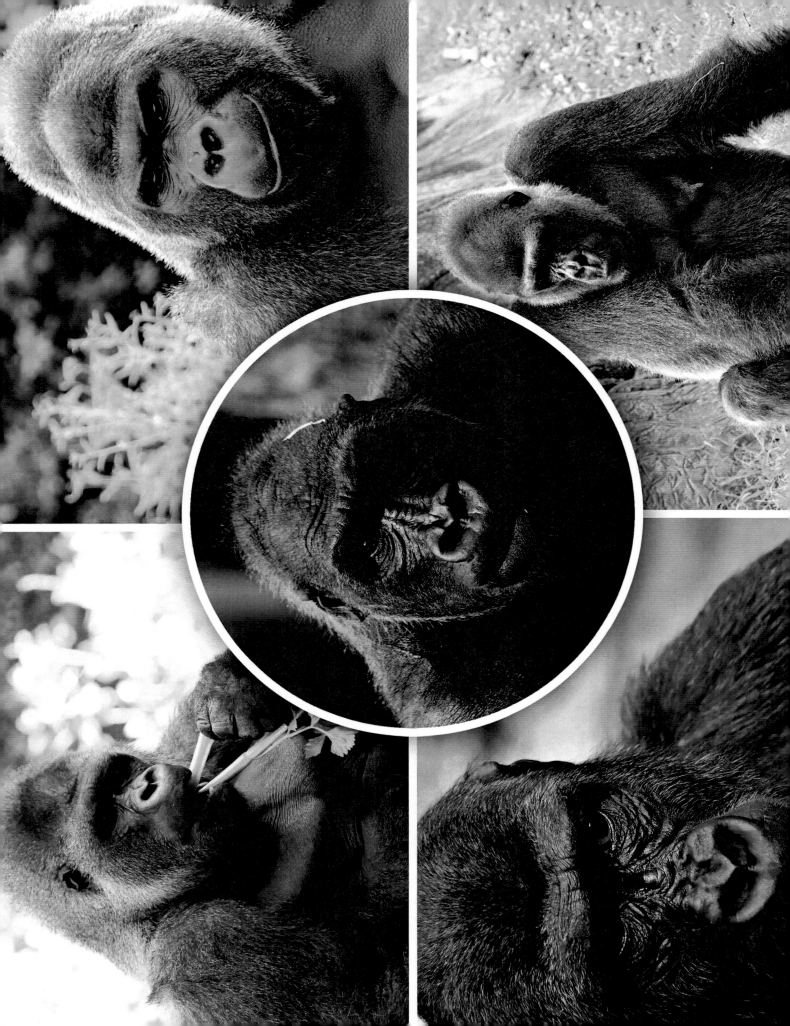

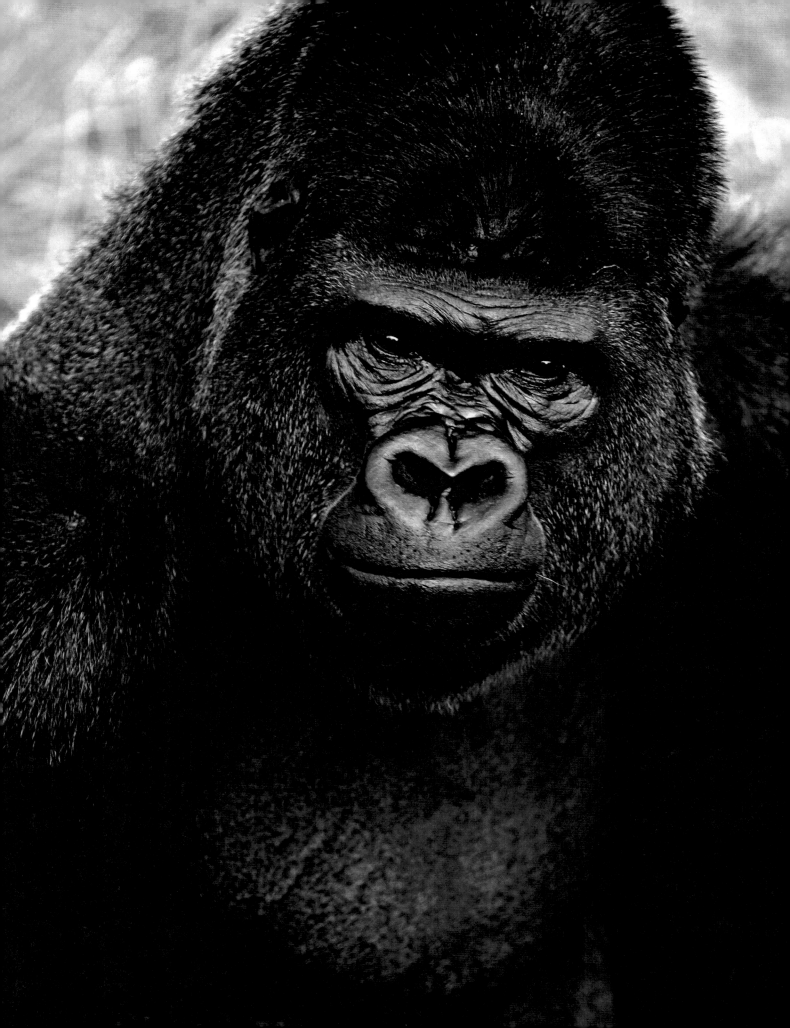

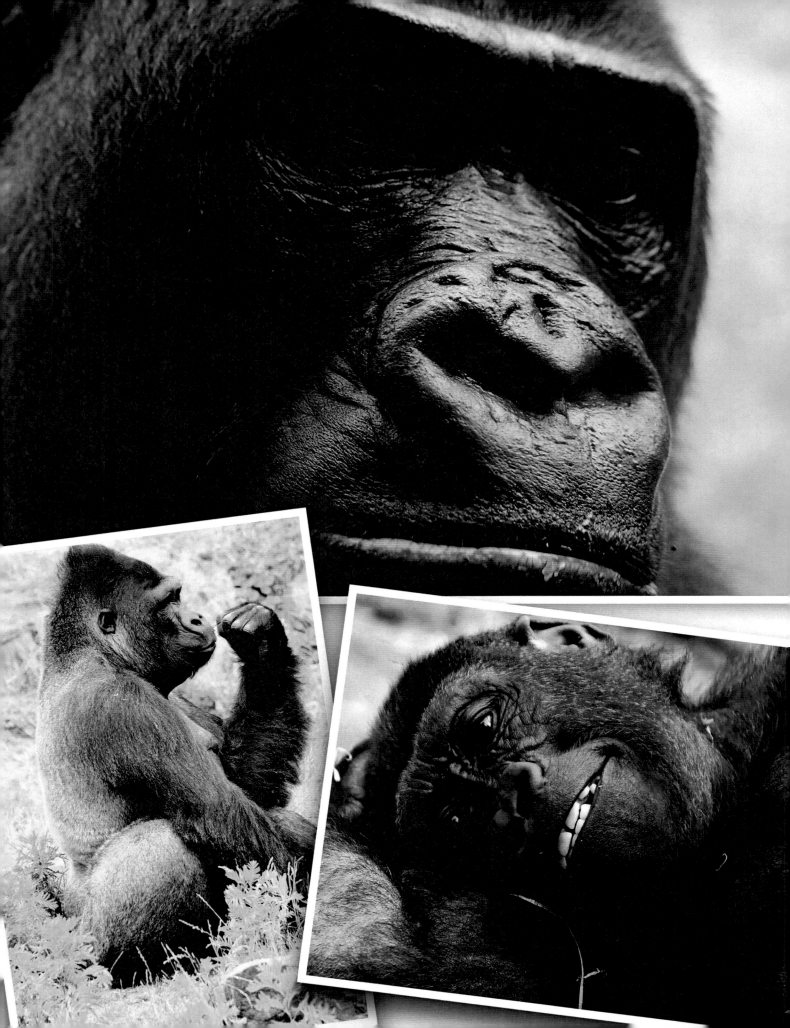

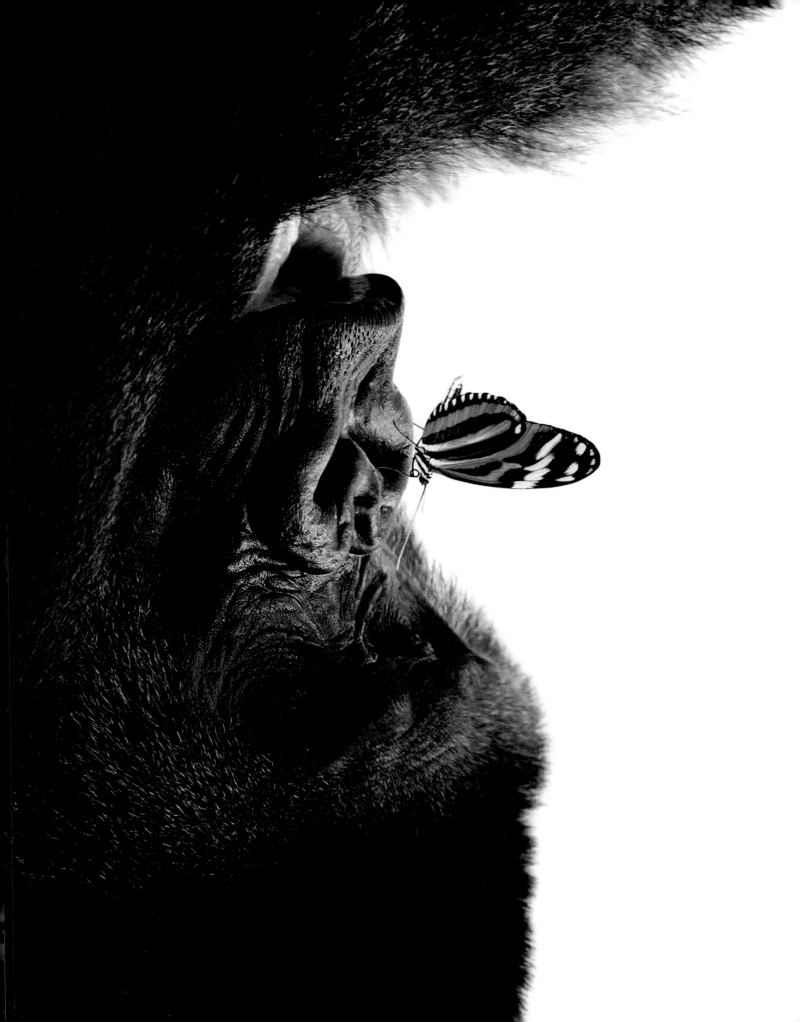

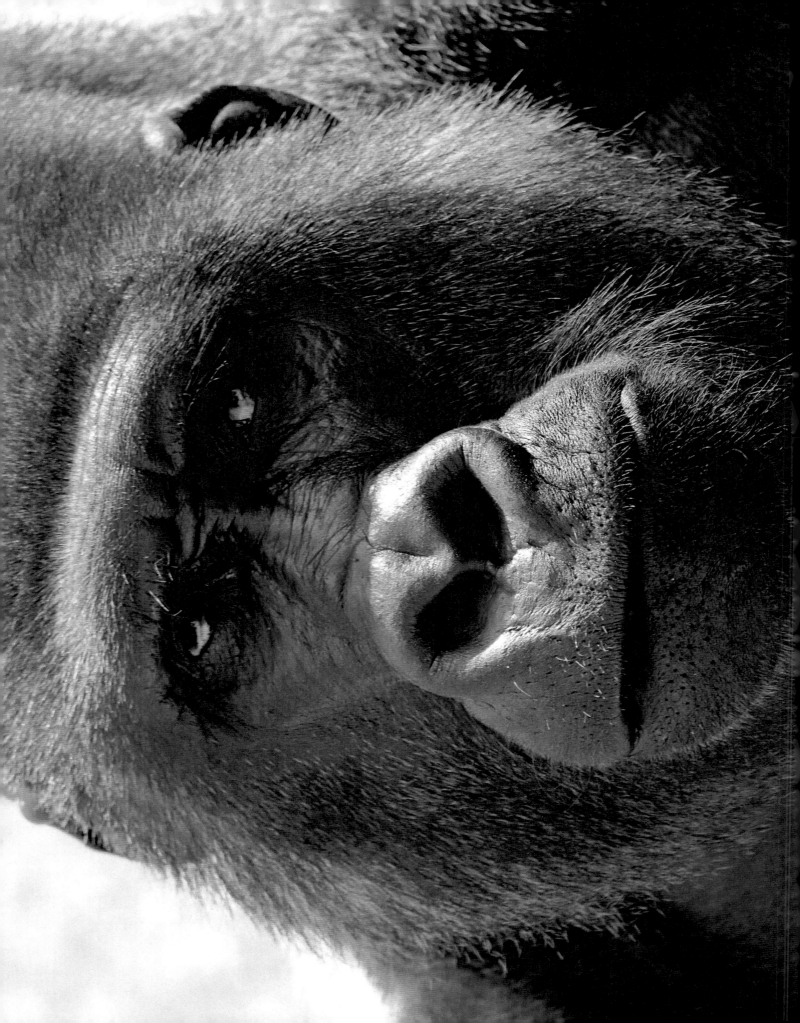

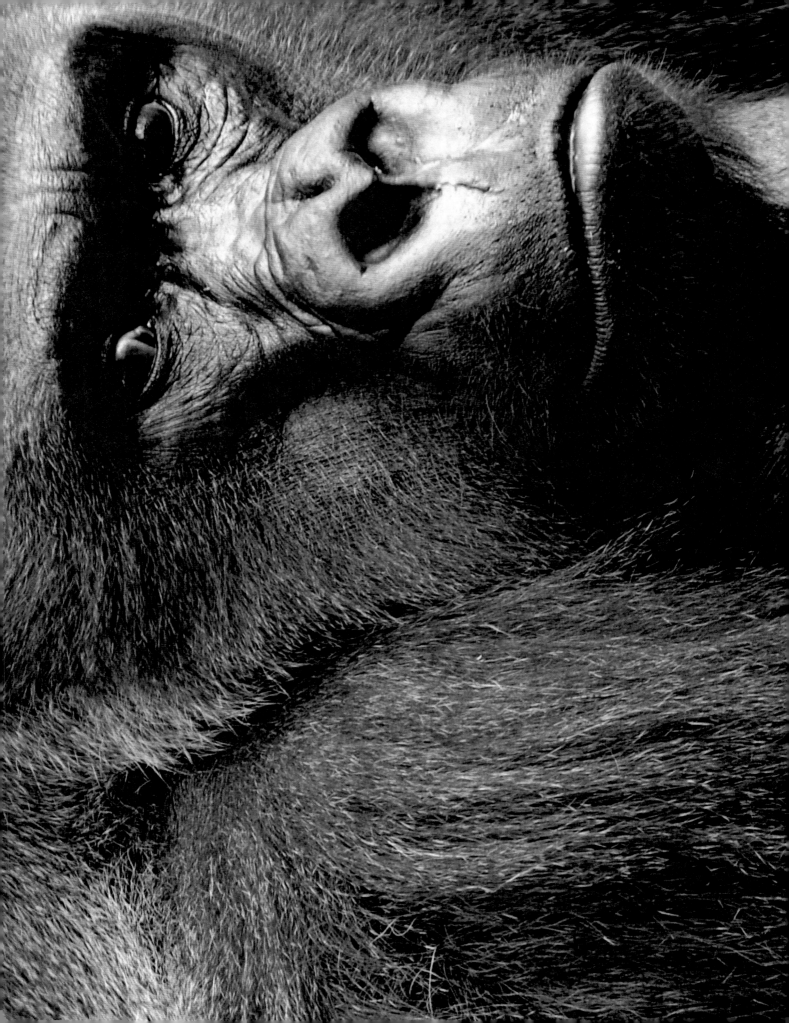

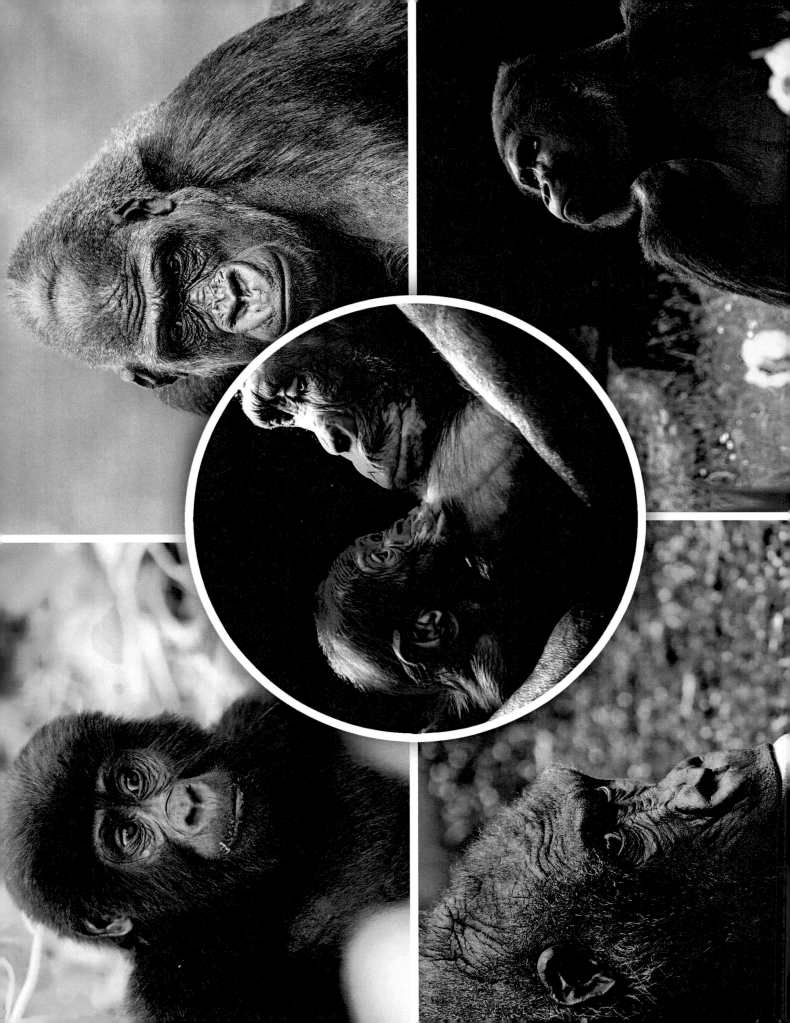

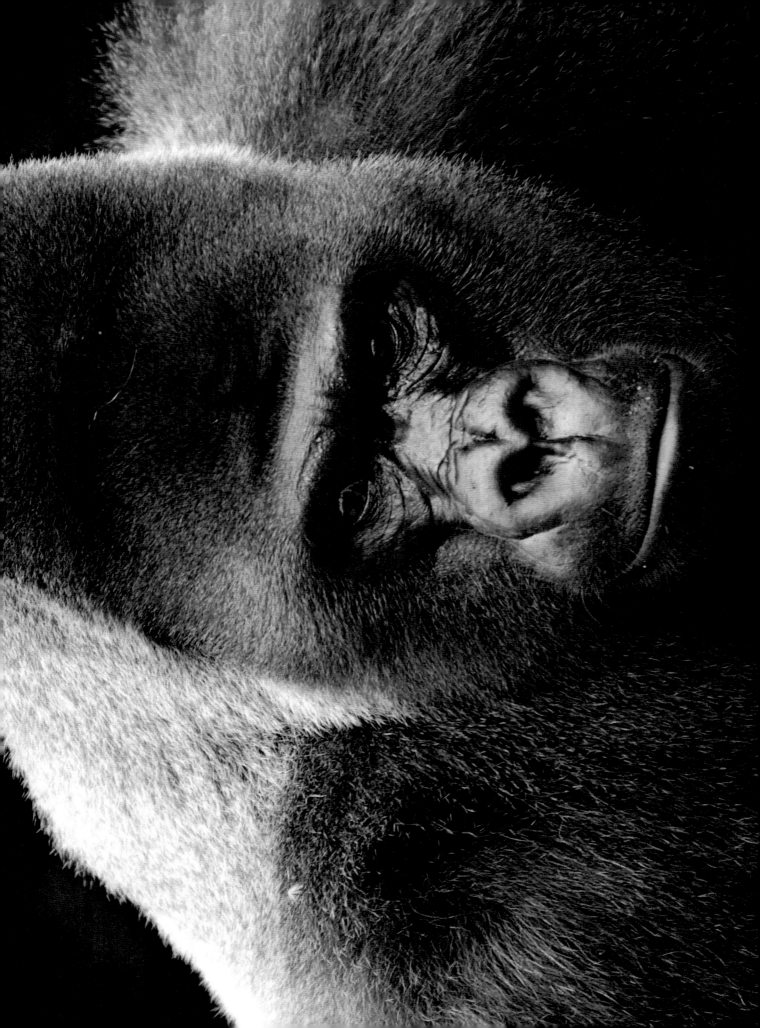

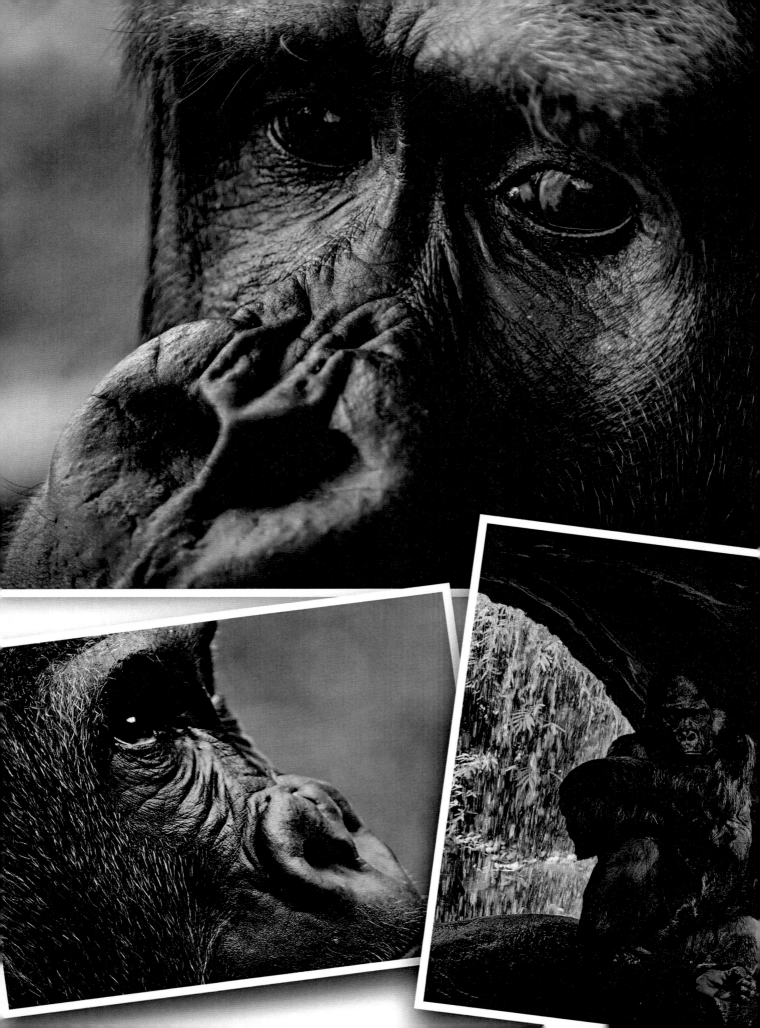

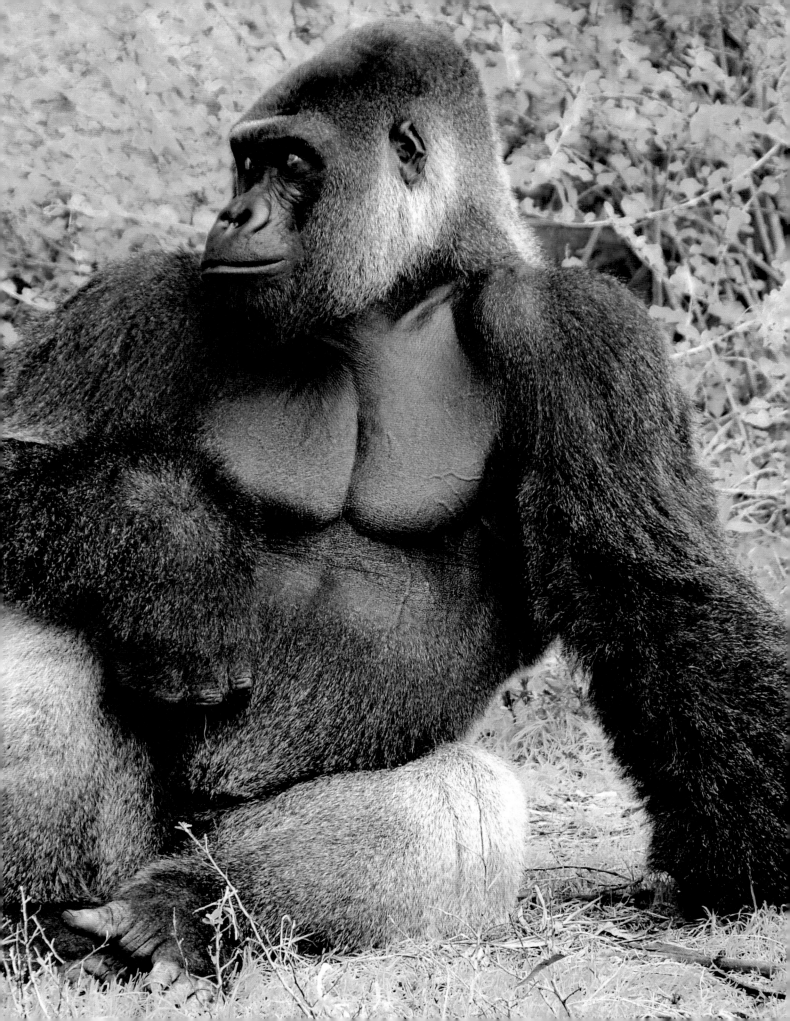

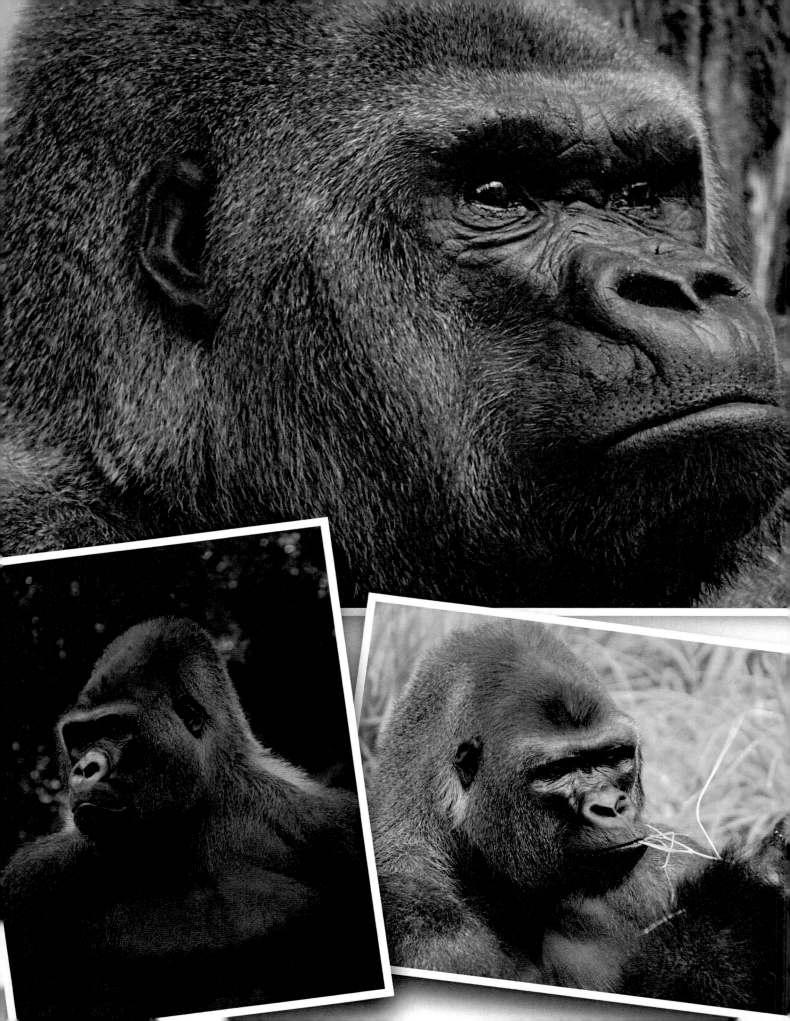

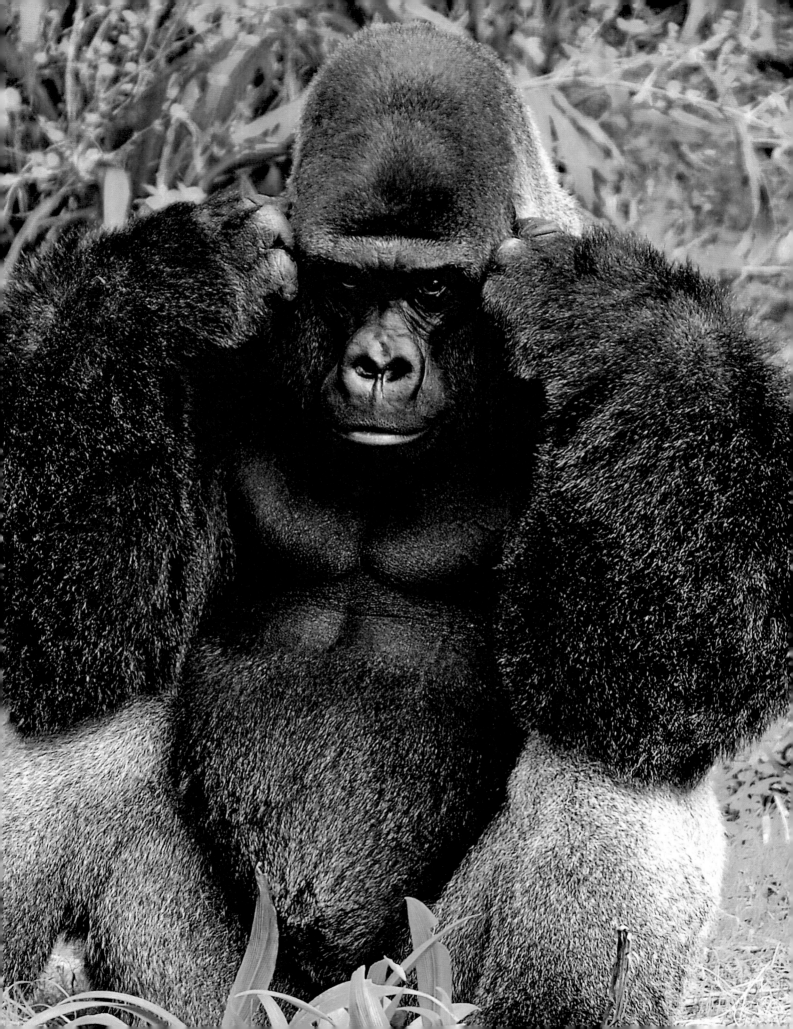

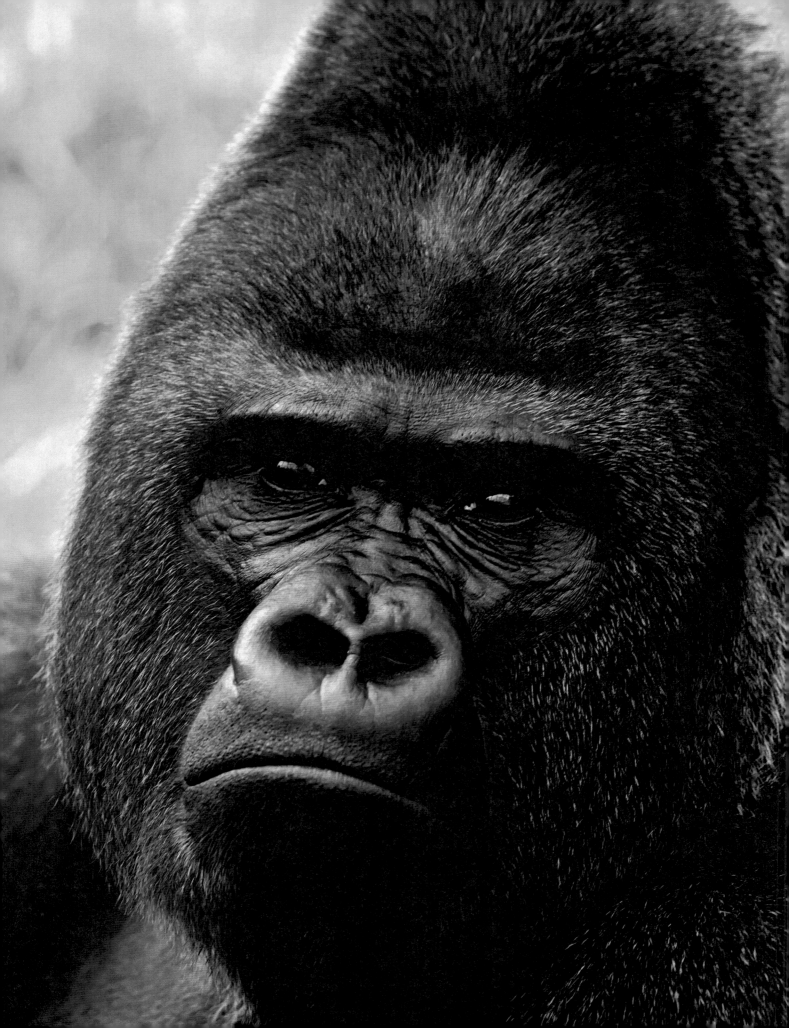

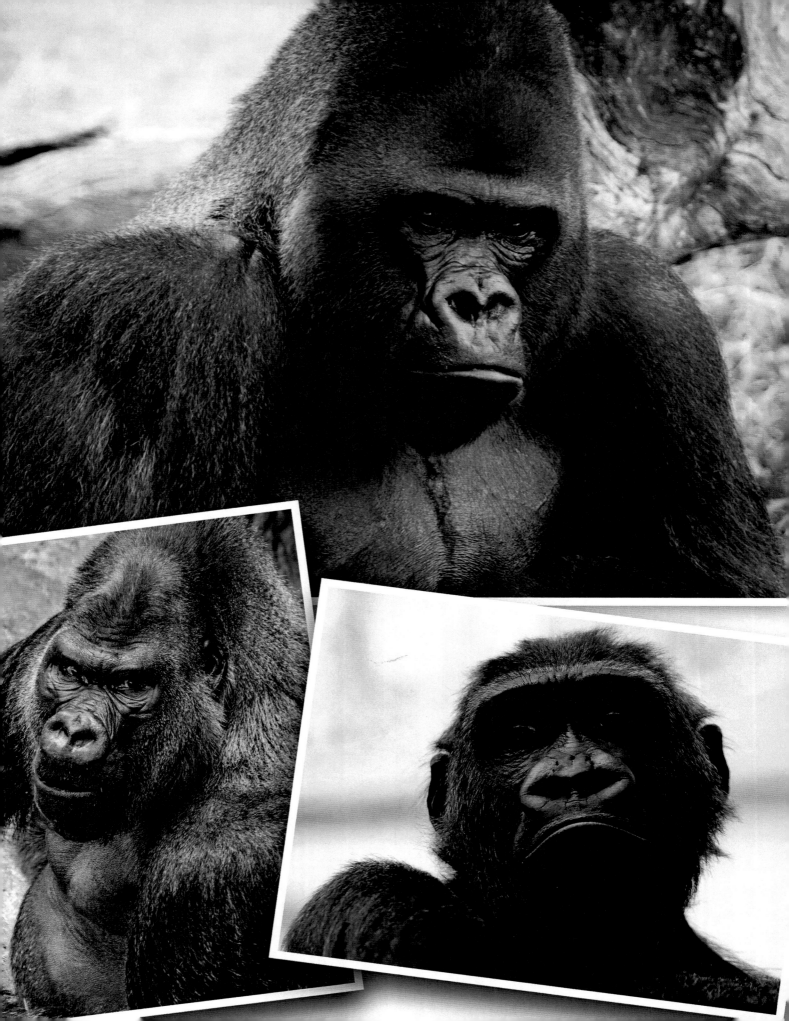

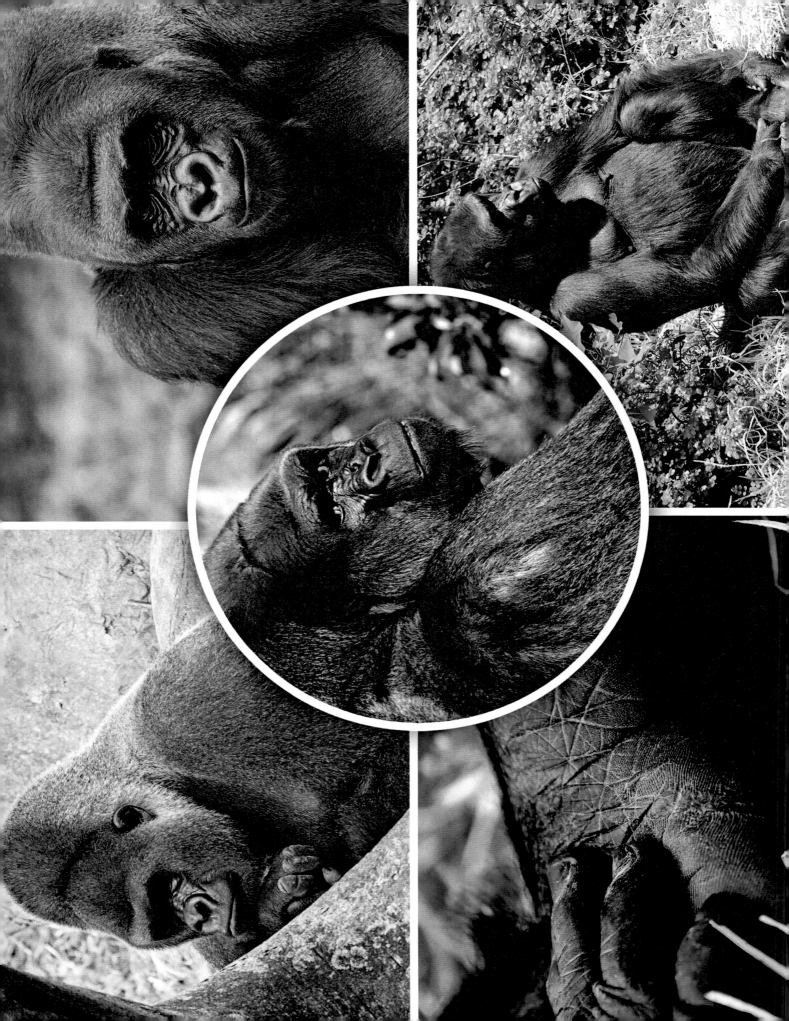

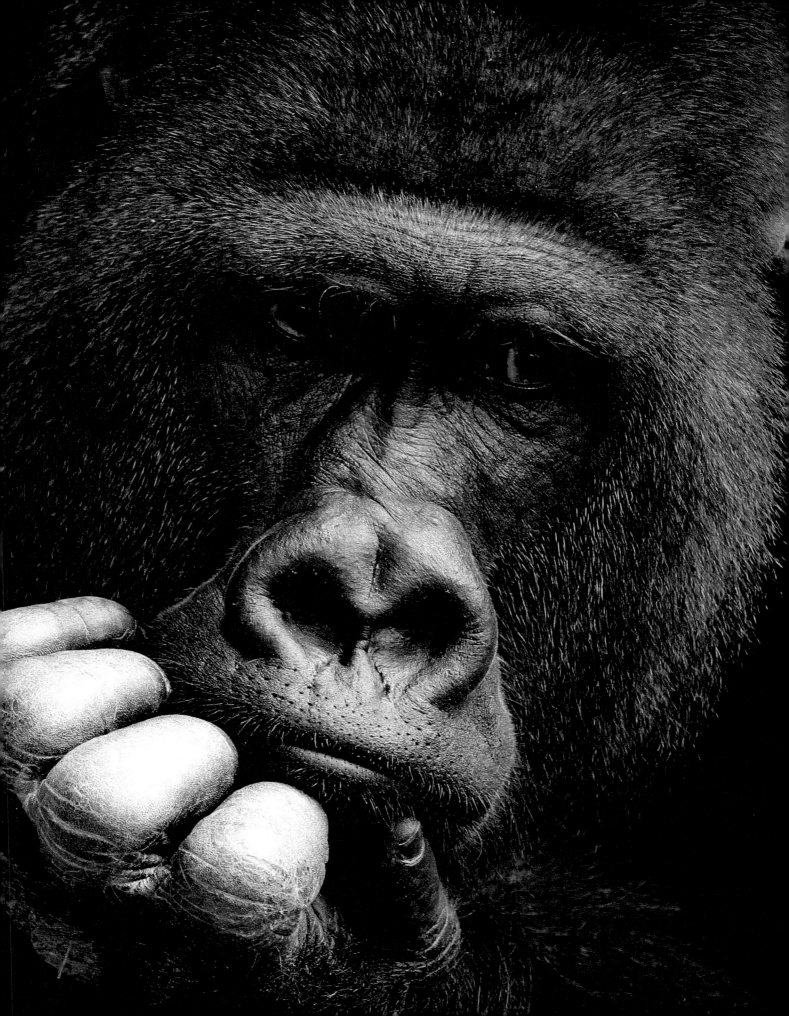

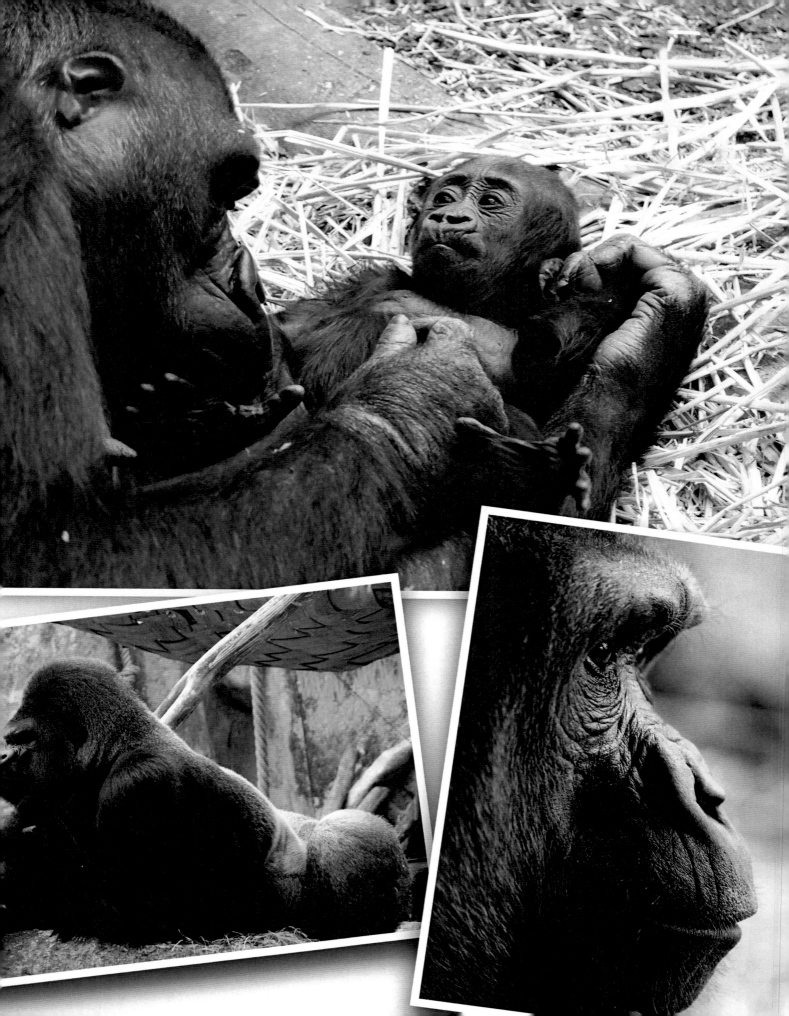

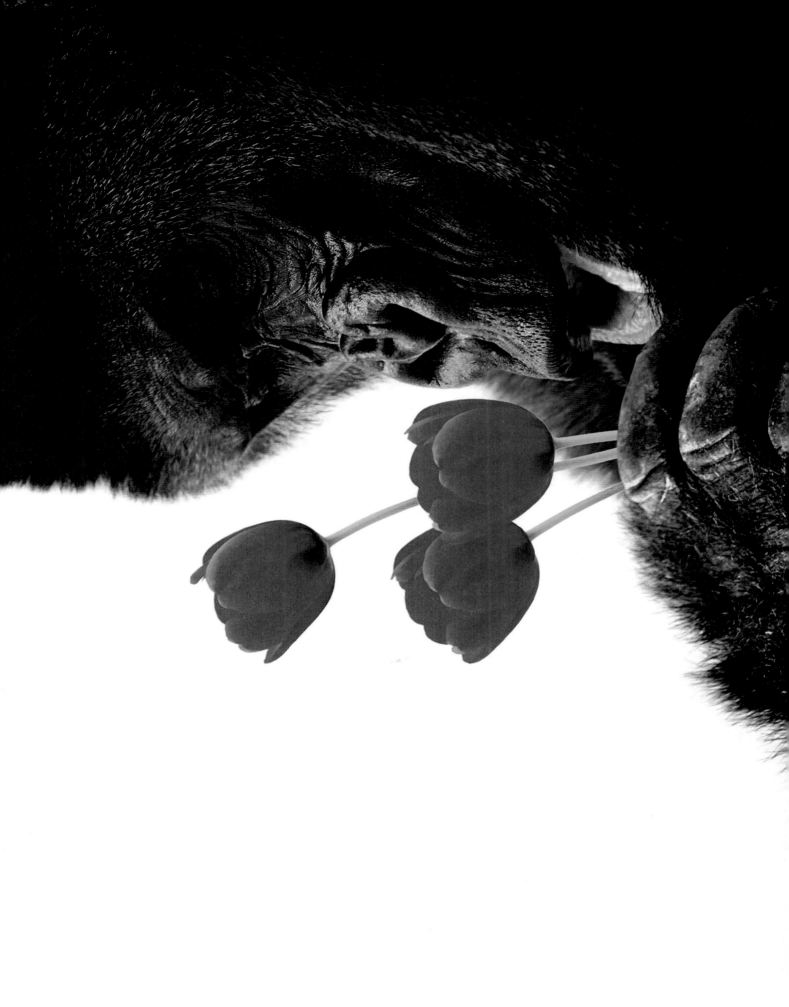

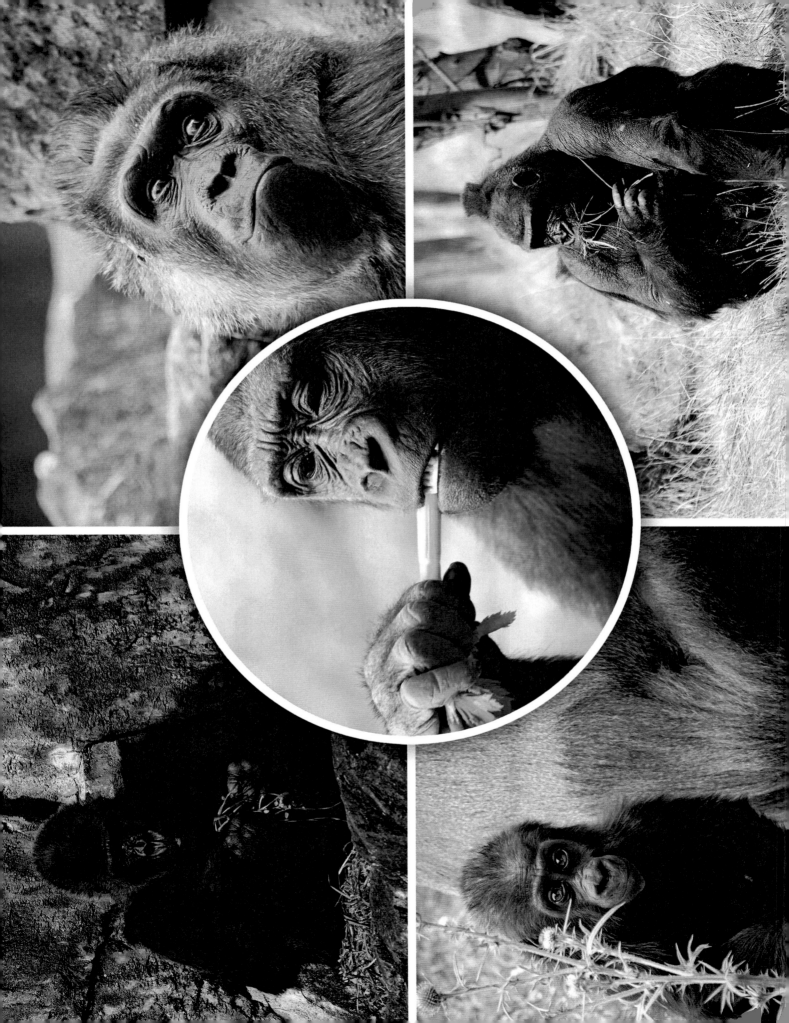

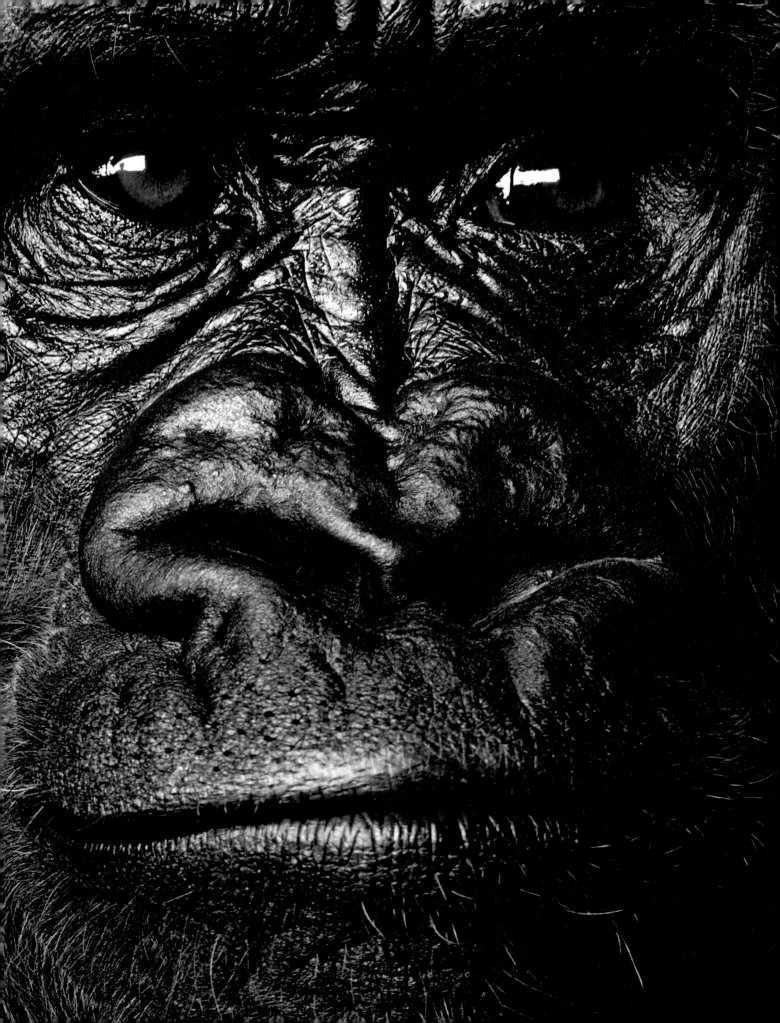

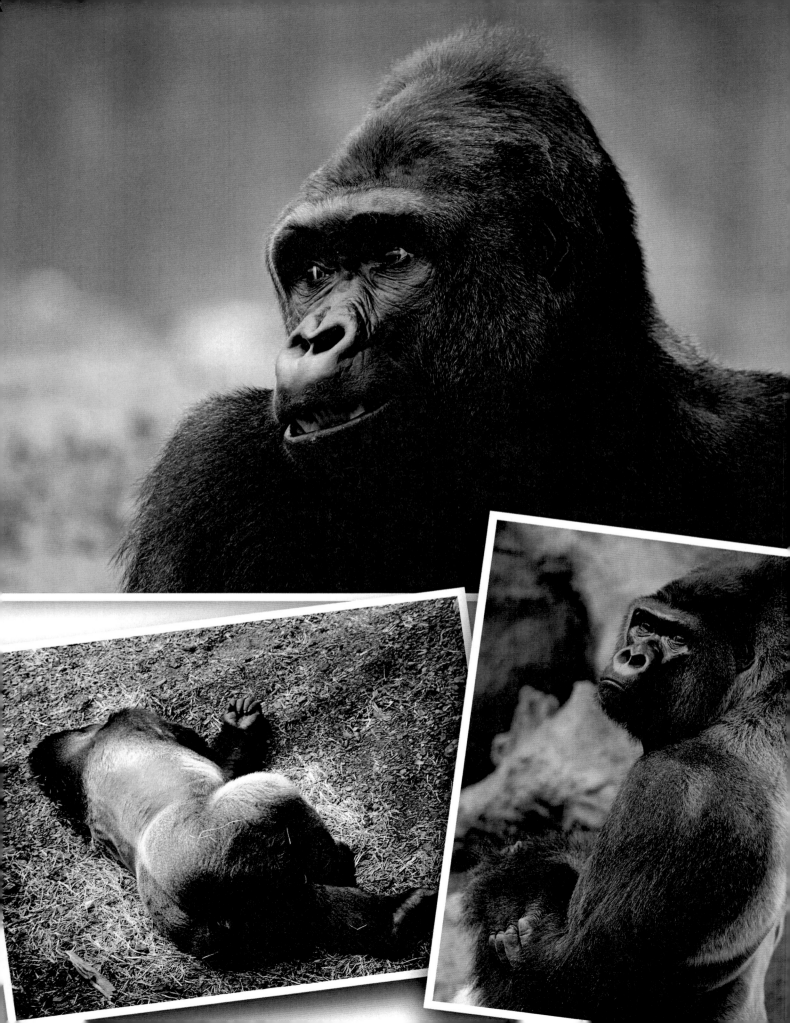

Made in United States
North Haven, CT
22 April 2023

35751076R10029